Below: A battery of SU-76M light SP guns advance during the fighting in Austria in the spring of 1945. The first digit probably refers to the regiment, while the other two refer to the battery and individual vehicle number. Since light artillery regiments at that time had only four batteries, it is likely that this numbering system was the reverse of the usual, with the final digit indicating the battery, and the middle digit being the individual vehicle number. (Sovfoto)

THE EASTERN FRONT

Armour Camouflage and Markings, 1941 to 1945

Steven J. Zaloga and James Grandsen

ARMS AND
ARMOUR

Contents

Published in Great Britain in 1983 by
Arms and Armour Press
Villiers House,
41-47 Strand,
London WC2N 5JE
A Cassell imprint

Reprinted 1989
Paperback edition 1993
Reprinted 1994
Reprinted 1995

Distributed in the USA by Sterling Publishing Co. Inc., 387 Park Avenue South, New York, NY 10016-8810.
Distributed in Australia by Capricorn Link (Australia) Pty. Ltd., 2/13 Carrington Road, Castle Hill, NSW 2154.

British Library Cataloguing in Publication Data:
Zaloga, Steven J.
The Eastern Front. – (Squadron signal)
1. Germany. *Heer* 2. Camouflage (Military science)
3. Vehicles, Military – Markings 4. World War, 1939-1945 – Campaigns – Soviet Union
I. Title II. Grandsen, James III. Series
355.8'3 UG449

ISBN 1-85409-213-8

Colour artwork by Bruce Culver and Steven J. Zaloga.
Edited by Tessa Rose.
Designed by Anthony A. Evans.
Typeset by Typesetters (Birmingham) Limited.
Printed and bound in Singapore by Craft Print Ltd.

Left: A column of Pz Kpfw IIs of the 11. Panzer Division are led down a Yugoslav road by an Sd Kfz 254 command vehicle. The Sd Kfz 254 displays a full range of markings typical of German armoured vehicles in the early stages of the war on the Eastern Front. On the left of the vehicle's bow can be seen the unofficial divisional insignia of the 11. Panzer Division, the wheeled ghost in white, while at upper right is the official divisional insignia, a divided yellow circle. Below the divisional insignia is a tactical map insignia in white indicating that the vehicle belongs to one of the division's towed howitzer batteries. (National Archives)

Preface

In the Dark Ages, the Teutonic knights waged their bloody wars in Eastern Europe ostensibly to convert the heathen Slavs. The emblem on their armour was the Christian cross. Seven centuries later when the Soviet Union was invaded by Germany and her allies, again the dominant emblem was the cross, whether the German Balkan cross, the Hungarian tricoloured cross, the Finnish hakaristi or the Romanian Michael's cross. Besides these ancient symbols, there were the emblems of more contemporary quasi-religions, Nazism, Fascism, Communism, and extreme nationalism. Antagonisms in this part of the world have long historical roots, and so too do the symbols of war.

In attempting to document the heraldry of mechanized warfare in Eastern Europe during the Second World War, the authors ran into two seemingly contradictory problems: too much information, and too little. In the case of German armoured vehicle markings, there has been so much specialized literature published that it is difficult to cram every available detail into the relatively confined space of one book. As a result, we have tried to provide a broad outline in the text, with the illustrations and photographs providing the details. Apart from Germany, in the case of virtually every other country covered in this book, there has been hardly anything of any real value published in English, except for scattered articles in the enthusiast magazines. Indeed, most military buffs are hardly aware of the employment of armoured vehicles by Bulgaria, Czechoslovakia, Finland or many of the other allied states of the great powers in the Second World War. It has been our intention to pay special attention here to these little-known combatants, and brief surveys are given of the use of armoured forces by some of the more obscure countries.

The great enigma, of course, is the Soviet Union, whose paranoid anxiety for military secrecy makes research on military subjects very difficult, even those from an historical perspective such as this. The problem has been compounded by the legendary murkiness of published Soviet histories, which has made a formidable task of tracing even the handful of unit insignia shown here. Equally challenging has been the collection of photographs of armoured vehicles of the East European states allied to Nazi Germany during the war. To the current Communist régimes, the history of their war against Soviet Russia is an acute embarrassment, and something to be suppressed.

The authors have received the kind and generous support of many fellow enthusiasts in compiling this book. We would like to thank Vika Edwards of Sovfoto, and Paul White of the Still Photos Branch, National Archives, for their kind aid in tracking down photographs used in the Soviet and German sections. Our thanks also go to Esa Muikku for his extensive help on the Finnish section, Janusz Magnuski on the Polish section, Ivan Bajtos on the Slovak and Hungarian sections, J. C. Probst on the Hungarian section and Jiri Hornat on the Czech section. Our gratitude is also expressed to George Balin, Tom Jentz, Kalevi Moilanen, David List and Istvan Batory. The colour illustrations were prepared by Bruce Culver and Steven Zaloga, and the small unit insignia drawings are by Steven Zaloga.

Steven J. Zaloga and James Grandsen, 1983.

Left: The crew of a KV-1 s ekranami heavy tank pose in front of their freshly decorated vehicle. The slogan chalked on the turret 'Pobeda budet za nami' ('Victory will be ours') was typical of the style of marking that became popular in Russian units during the war. (Sovfoto)

Right: A Panzerbefehlswagen I (foreground) and Hanomag Sd Kfz 251 on a muddy street in Yugoslavia during the brief campaign there prior to the invasion of the Soviet Union in June 1941. These vehicles belong to the 11. Panzer Division and are finished in dark grey overall with tactical markings in white and yellow. In the case of the Pz Bf Wg I, the markings consist of a white Balkan cross, a yellow circle (probably indicating 2nd Battalion) and a yellow tactical number, 04. (National Archives)

Germany

The Wehrmacht employed one of the most complicated and comprehensive systems of combat vehicle markings of all the belligerents in the Second World War. Vehicle markings often mirrored German fortunes on the Eastern Front. In the heady days of 'Barbarossa', German tanks were adorned gaudily in national markings and heraldic unit insignia, in cavalier disregard of counter-intelligence requirements. But, as the war started to turn in favour of the Soviet Union after Stalingrad in January 1943, far more prudence was shown and markings began to disappear. Mimetic camouflage painting was introduced in 1943 and, finally, in 1944 orders were issued forbidding the use of heraldic divisional insignia.

Camouflage Painting

During Operation 'Barbarossa' in the summer of 1941, German armoured vehicles were finished in the same fashion as they had been in Poland in 1939 and France in 1940: panzer grey overall. This colour was a very dark blue grey and covered the entire exterior of the vehicle, including the inner faces of hatches that opened outward. The only other major colours used on armoured vehicles were a light cream paint used in the enclosed spaces of the fighting compartment interior, and a red oxide primer, used mainly as an undercoat and usually not evident. The Wehrmacht was caught largely unprepared for the bitter 1941–42 winter fighting, and most units were obliged to improvise winter snow camouflage for their vehicles. Paint was seldom available, leading to the use of lime whitewash, chalk, and even white cloth. In subsequent winter campaigns,

ample supplies of a lime/salt whitewash and other coatings were made available. There was no supply of proper painting equipment in the winter of 1941, leading to the use of brooms, buckets or rags and, as a result, the application was often ragged in appearance.

German armour retained the panzer grey overall finish (with its seasonal white moult) until 18 February 1943 when a new camouflage system was introduced by HM 1943 Nr. 181. The new base colour, called dark yellow, was a greyish mustard that had a tendency to fade to a very light greyish sand shade. In addition, units were issued with two more colours, a drab olive green and a red brown which could be applied over the base dark yellow to create disruptive camouflage patterns. These colours were supplied in 2kg or 20kg tins. The new colours were reminiscent of those shades used by the German Army in 1918 or by the French and Polish armoured forces in 1939–40. No instructions were issued regarding the patterns in which the new colours were to be painted, and this was left to the discretion of unit commanders to permit them to adapt the schemes to local terrain coloration. The additional two colours were provided in a paste form that was diluted with petrol, kerosene or water. The latter was to be used only in emergencies because the paint finish that resulted from using water as a solvent was not durable enough to survive heavy rain. New armoured vehicles arrived from the factories painted in dark yellow overall, and older vehicles were gradually repainted as they were overhauled.

The new camouflage system potentially offered the benefit of flexibility in matching a vehicle's coloration

Opposite page, top: A Pz Kpfw III als Tauchpanzer submersible tank after the crossing of the Bug River near Patulin on 22 June 1941 in the opening hours of Operation 'Barbarossa'. In addition to the tactical number, it bears the official divisional insignia of the 18. Panzer Division and, above it, the black and white unofficial insignia of the 18. Panzer Brigade, appropriately enough a skull above waves.

Opposite page, bottom: This damaged 15cm sIG33 (Sf) auf Pz Kpfw IB displays the divisional marking of the 10. Panzer Division, a yellow Y with three strokes, and the number above it refers to sIG Kompanie 706 to which it was attached. The Balkan cross shows one of the many detail variations of this national insignia.

Top: A Panzer IV Ausf E of the 12. Panzer Division during fighting in Russia on 9 July 1941. The divisional insignia is evident both on the front and side, as well as the national insignia on the hull side, broken by the radio mast tray. Although by 1941 most German tanks carried their tactical numbers painted conspicuously on the turret, this tank retains the old 1939—40 system of painting the number (32) on a small rhomboid plate attached to the side aft the Balkan cross.

Middle: Some German units had insignia uniquely their own, such as this Pz Kpfw II of the Panzer Abteilung 100 (F). This flamethrower unit used an insignia consisting of three thin concentric bands on the turret rear.

Bottom: Ground-attack aircraft are notorious for strafing their own troops and vehicles by mistake, and so care is usually taken to provide armoured vehicles with some means of national identification. German forces on the Eastern Front generally used the red/white/black Nazi flag, as in the case of this Hanomag Sd Kfz 251 crew. In some panzer grenadier units, the half-tracks used tactical numbers in the same fashion as tanks, even though this did not become standard practice until the April 1944 orders.

to the local terrain, but this potential often was not realized. Indeed, during the 1943–44 campaigns, much of the Wehrmacht's armoured vehicle inventory remained finished in plain pale mustard, which was far from ideal for operations in temperate Europe as the vehicles were easily identifiable by air or when observed at ground level against the darker terrain colouration. The system's main problem was that it relied on the initiative of the crews themselves, who were frequently too encumbered with more important tasks to bother with vehicle camouflage. A German veteran remarked that the spray equipment provided for applying camouflage paint was the second item tossed overboard from armoured vehicles after the equally treasured gas masks. As the supply system deteriorated, paint was given little priority and even when available often had to be used with sub-standard solvents, such as water, since fuel was so precious. Application was frequently careless, with the paint so thin that the resulting patterns had little disruptive effect and were good for hardly more than crew morale. Some units had better luck with the system by painting whole companies of tanks at one time, usually during rest and refit breaks behind the lines where greater care could be taken.

The problems with the 1943 system seem to have been appreciated, and in the final year of the war the Wehrmacht appear to have introduced a new system or at least new policies concerning the application of camouflage finishes. During this period, German armoured vehicles began sporting a modified version of the 1943 scheme, using the same colours but applied in a more consistent pattern. The vehicles began to be painted with thick, distinct bands of the green and brown secondary colours, with the bands speckled with small dots or bars of the dark yellow colour. This pattern is often called 'ambush scheme' since it proved particularly effective on vehicles lurking in wooded areas

where the pattern resembled the effect of light speckling on the forest floor. Although there has not been any written evidence to verify it, it is the authors' opinion that during this period the Wehrmacht decided to adopt the Luftwaffe's policy of having disruptive camouflage patterns applied at the factory or other centralized locations to ensure more rigid compliance with camouflage directives. The 'ambush pattern' was not the only scheme in use at this time, but its complexity and widespread use among units broadly scattered on both the Eastern and Western Front lends credence to the supposition that a more centralized control over camouflage painting was exerted in 1945.

As the war drew to its bloody climax, logistics in the Wehrmacht supply chain began to crack. Old supplies of panzer grey paint were used when the standard dark yellow was no longer available. For example, a colour photograph survives of a Möbelwagen finished in panzer grey overall camouflaged with bands of red-brown paint. Besides these occasional eccentricities in Germany itself, vehicles under manufacture in Czechoslovakia, such as the Hetzer, began to appear in Czech Army paint which consisted of dark green overall with cream and dark brown swaths.

Painted disruptive camouflage is only marginally effective even in ideal circumstances, and the Wehrmacht on the Eastern Front frequently employed other, sometimes more successful techniques. Foliage and tree branches perhaps are the best form of disruptive camouflage, albeit rather short-lived in effectiveness. In desperation, mud was sometimes used to create disruptive patterns over panzer grey or dark yellow finishes. One surface finish peculiar to German armoured vehicles was Zimmerit paste, a concrete plaster applied to tank superstructures and turrets to prevent the attachment of magnetic mines by Soviet infantry. This did not affect the colour of the vehicle

Top left: A StuG III Ausf F of StuG Brigade 210, known as the 'Tigerkopf Brigade' because of the unit's distinctive brigade insignia, which is evident here. The brigade was heavily involved in the fighting in the Caucasus, and this view from 1943 shows the assault gun in the new 1943 scheme of dark yellow with olive green over-spray. Besides the tiger's head insignia on the bow and side, the battery letter, 'F', is also clearly visible.

Left: A fine study of a Pz Kpfw IV Ausf H showing the 1943 camouflage system. The base dark yellow has been over-sprayed with splotchy bands of red-brown and dark olive green. The markings consist of a simple, white, hollow Balkan cross, a hollow stencilled tactical number on the turret skirts and, to the upper left of the cross, a black railroad loading label. This photograph is believed to have been taken during the Kursk offensive in the summer of 1943. (National Archives)

Top right: A Pz Kpfw III Ausf J of the 5. SS Panzer Division Wiking during the drive on Stalingrad through the Caucasus in the autumn of 1942. The divisional insignia is evident on the left mudguard. This vehicle was finished in panzer grey, but dust has given it a lighter appearance and obscured the large three-digit tactical number on the turret.

Centre right: The first Tiger to be lost on the Eastern Front was this vehicle of sPzAbt 502, knocked out near Rabochii Poselek No. 5 outside Leningrad on 13 January 1942. It still retains the panzer grey overall finish of the period, and on the turret rear is the unit's famous elephant insignia. The vehicle number is carried on the stowage bin.

Bottom right: A symbol of the German defeat in the Kursk offensive has long been the ill-fated Ferdinands (Sturmgeschütz mit 8.8cm PaK 43/2, Sd Kfz 184, also called Elefants) of Jagd-Regiment 656. This disabled vehicle is finished in dark yellow overall with a curious pattern of dark olive green typical of the Ferdinands at Kursk. Of 89 Ferdinands available at the start of the offensive, 39 were lost.

Left: In contrast with other heavy tank battalion Tigers shown here, this Tiger I, photographed in the summer of 1943, shows the 1943 camouflage colours applied in a very distinct and effective disruptive pattern of red-brown and olive green over dark yellow. The unit is not known. (National Archives)

Below left: Although many vehicles taking part in the Kursk offensive sported the new three-tone 1943 scheme, some vehicles, such as this 3.7cm FlaK36 auf Fgst Zgkw 5t, were finished overall in the older dark grey scheme, over which small swaths of dark yellow have been added. Barely evident on the right-hand corner of the trailer rear is the trident emblem of 2. Panzer Division. (National Archives)

Right: As is quite evident in this head-on shot of a Tiger I in 1943, the 1943 camouflage system was applied with varying results by different units. On this vehicle, the dark green over-spray seems so diluted that it is barely noticeable and has little disruptive effect. The unit insignia on the glacis is as yet unidentified. The tactical number on the turret is 214. (National Archives)

since the Zimmerit was usually applied at the factory prior to painting, but it gave German armoured vehicles a distinct appearance due to the patterns in which it was applied. The application of Zimmerit was confined mainly to tanks and assault guns from 1943 to late 1944, by which time its use was abandoned.

National Insignia

The Wehrmacht and other German forces (Waffen SS and Luftwaffe ground divisions) used the Balkan cross as the standard national insignia for armoured vehicles during the war. Its proportions and colours differed, in early 1941 often being only a simplified white border form against the dark panzer grey camouflage, while later appearing in the more conventional form of a black cross with white border, sometimes edged in black. Generally, the crosses were quite small, seldom exceeding 6in, and there was some standardization of positioning. On tanks, the cross was generally found on either hull side and once on the rear. It was seldom seen on the turret but there were some exceptions, such as the Tiger II. The positioning was similar on self-propelled guns and other armoured vehicles. Although usually centrally located on the side, on some tanks, such as the Panther, it was generally carried far forward since the presence of stowage at the middle of the hull made its positioning there unpractical. On captured vehicles it was usually the practice to paint national insignia quite large.

For air identification, the Wehrmacht initially tried insignia painted on turret roofs, but this was inadequate and led to the widespread use of the red, white and black Nazi flag. Late in April 1945, some German tanks began to sport painted white roof crosses in an attempt to mimic Soviet air identity markings of the time and so to give some protection against roaming Allied ground-attack aircraft. The ruse was discovered and, conse-

quently, the Soviets adopted another symbol in May. Although German soft-skin vehicles and unarmoured half-tracks ordinarily did not use painted Balkan crosses, they did use flags for air identity purposes.

Unit Insignia

The German armed forces used heraldic insignia to a much greater extent than any other army bar the British. These insignia first began as simple geometric designs assigned by the OKH, but as the war dragged on many units devised their own, often quite elaborate formation signs. On some tanks, not only was an official divisional insignia evident, but sometimes an unofficial panzer regiment crest as well. Probably the most elaborate divisional insignia was the white clock circle of the Herman Göring Division, which had a clock hand pointing to the number indicating the sub-formation. The clock hand itself was painted in the branch colour, which in the case of panzer troops was black. Therefore, a clock face with the hand pointing to 1 o'clock indicated the 1st company, and the black colour of the clock hand indicated a panzer battalion. The HQ company pointed to noon and had a prominent dot in the centre. A major problem faced by the Wehrmacht on the Eastern Front was the prying eyes of hostile resistance groups, which observed vehicle markings to build up accurate order of battle assessments for Soviet and Allied intelligence. In an attempt to confuse enemy intelligence gathering, the Germans occasionally adopted temporary insignia, the best known of which were probably those of the SS panzer divisions in 1943 around the time of the Kursk offensive. The major divisional insignia are shown on p. 49, though it should be kept in mind that details and coloration of these insignia varied.

The casual disregard for counter-intelligence evident in the leisurely use of easily decipherable unit insignia

Top left: No painted camouflage is as effective as the use of natural camouflage, utilized here by a Wespe of the 2. Panzer Division in 1943. The division's trident insignia is barely discernible on the armour shield immediately in front of the small log. (National Archives)

Below left: A rather battered Pz Kpfw IV Ausf G of sPzAbt 502 with a Tiger of the same unit during the fighting in the summer of 1943. The battalion insignia, a white elephant, is evident on the rear turret stowage box. Turret numbers were often applied with stencils, and while the Tiger has had the gaps cleanly filled in, on the Pz Kpfw IV the original broken style was retained. (National Archives)

Top right: Pz Kpfw IV Ausf Hs of Panzer Regiment 3, 2. Panzer Division advance during the fighting in the summer of 1943. These vehicles have a distinctive camouflage pattern of dark olive green over dark yellow. Tactical numbers are carried only on the turret rear; on the turret skirt front is the regimental insignia, which is shown in the colour plates on p. 48. The divisional insignia, a white trident, is carried to the left of the Balkan cross.

Centre right: After the Kursk offensive in the summer of 1943, German tanks began to receive coatings of Zimmerit anti-magnetic mine paste. Initially, this was applied in the field with an uneven effect, as in this Panther Ausf D. Indeed, the texture obscures the light over-spray of red-brown and olive green. This Panther belonged to the first battalion headquarters of a panzer regiment, evident by the use of the A letter code serving as a prefix to the tactical number. This style of A/B was less common than the I/II prefixes.

Bottom right: An Sd Kfz 250/5 leichter Beobachtungspanzer-wagen of Artillerie Regiment 74, 2. Panzer Division during the 1943 Kursk offensive passing a disabled Soviet ZiS-3 76.2mm field gun. Next to the divisional trident insignia is the tactical map insignia for a self-propelled howitzer battalion, painted in white on a dark green patch. The '1' on the right of the insignia indicates the 1st battalion; there were three battalions to a regiment. This vehicle is finished in a typical 1943 scheme. (National Archives)

Above: A Tiger I of 3. Kompanie of the SS Panzer Division Das Reich undergoes repairs to its exhaust system carried out by its crew. The vehicle is neatly finished in white winter camouflage overall, and carries the turret tactical number 332. (Joseph Desautels)

Left: Pz Kpfw IV Ausf Hs of one of the panzer divisions of the 48. Panzer Korps pass through burning Zhitomir during the brutal fighting against Rybalko's 3rd Guards Tank Army in January 1944. Tank 32 is finished in dark yellow overall. Its red or black tactical numbers on the side of the turret skirt are clearly evident.

gradually began to disappear through 1943 as the Wehrmacht suffered setback after setback. In January 1943, the OKH ordered all unit insignia to be painted out by units on the Western Front, an order that appears to have been extended to the Eastern Front sometime later in the year. It was not uniformly obeyed.

Although the OKH officially acknowledged only divisional insignia, some smaller formations, such as assault gun brigades (Sturmgeschütz), adopted their own insignia as well. Most Sturmgeschütz brigades had elaborate heraldic shield insignia, but in most cases when used on armoured vehicles the insignia were greatly simplified. Precise details of the colours used on these insignia have not been available in all cases, so the colouring of some of the insignia shown here should be regarded as speculative. The heavy tank battalions also adopted heraldic unit insignia, but they were only used occasionally and the majority of Tiger tanks went into combat devoid of distinctive unit insignia. The illustrations here show a comprehensive range of the insignia

Above: One marking occasionally seen on German armoured vehicles was the chassis (fahrgestell) number, evident here on the glacis plate (FG 96260), which identifies the vehicle as a 7.5cm StuG40 Ausf G. This number was often over-painted before the vehicle was issued to the troops.

Right: A battery of Wespes open fire from positions south of Berdichev during the bitter fighting in the Ukraine, 31 January 1944. In contrast to the 1941 campaign, by 1944 panzer units were better provided with white paint and whitewash with which to camouflage their vehicles for the winter fighting.

used by the heavy battalions, although some of their units saw little if any fighting on the Eastern Front.

Tactical Insignia
The German Army made widespread use of standard map symbols as a form of vehicle marking. These symbols were not widely used on tanks, but could be seen on assault guns, armoured half-tracks and tank destroyers. The system remained relatively constant through the course of the war, though in 1943 a slightly amended style was adopted which changed some of the symbols in detail. The entire system is not illustrated here due to most of the symbols being inapplicable to armoured vehicles, but some of the most common types are shown. The system has been widely dealt with, and those desiring a survey of the more esoteric symbols should consult some of the books and articles listed in the Bibliography on p. 96. These symbols, when carried, were usually painted on or near the mudguard so that they would be immediately visible to military policemen.

Top left: A Tiger of sPzAbt 502 on the Leningrad front in 1943. The tactical number 314 has been repeated on the turret side and on the side of the hull because of the stowage on the turret. This vehicle is finished plainly in dark yellow overall without any disruptive painting.

Centre left: A Pz Kpfw III Ausf J has its engine overhauled somewhere in the Ukraine, 10 February 1944. The tank is finished in a splotchy pattern of white over the summer camouflage colours. It has a simple black stencilled number on the turret.

Bottom left: Self-propelled howitzers such as this Hummel in Russia on 15 February 1944 usually carried battery letters, in this case 'A', in place of tactical numbers. However, the April 1944 markings orders instructed units to adopt tactical numbering akin to the style used on tanks throughout the war.

Opposite page, top: An Sd Kfz 232 similar to a great many German armoured vehicles fighting on the Eastern Front, painted simply in dark yellow overall with no disruptive camouflage. Immediately below the helmet on the hull side are railroad loading markings. The first line identifies the vehicle and the second and third give weight information. Usually, this marking was contained within a thin rectangular box insignia.

Opposite page, bottom: Luftwaffe flak vehicles, such as this 2cm FlaK38 auf Fgst Zgkw 8t (right), were finished similarly to Wehrmacht or Waffen SS combat vehicles. The vehicle licence plate with the WL prefix identifies it as a Luftwaffe vehicle. The Hanomag 251 Ausf D (left) of the Panzer Lehr Division carries the usual WH (Wehrmacht) prefix. This photograph was taken in the centre of Budapest in late spring 1944.

Top left: A pair of Panthers and a schwere Panzerspähwagen 7.5cm Sd Kfz 233 of SS Panzer Division Wiking during operations in the Kampinos forest north of Warsaw in August 1944. The Panther on the right, a Panzerbefehlswagen Panther command tank, carries the tactical numbering I03 on the turret side, indicative of a signals officer's tank, 1st battalion HQ company of a panzer regiment.

Centre left: A pair of Tigers of 1. Kompanie, sPzAbt 509 in action near Zhitomir in the Ukraine at the end of 1943. The sPzAbt 509 used this roman-style numbering rather than the gothic numbering style more typical of German tanks. The vehicle finish seems to be a broken pattern of white over the summer camouflage scheme.

Bottom left: A column of Marder II tank destroyers of an S anti-tank gun company of Panzer Grenadier Division Grossdeutschland in the early spring of 1944. These vehicles are finished in dark yellow overall. On the hull rear is evident the divisional insignia, a white helmet, and the tactical symbol for an SP anti-tank gun company in red or black. (Joseph Desautels)

Tactical Numbering

The German armed forces used a standardized form of turret tactical numbering on tanks and some other armoured vehicles. Each tank in a tank company would be assigned a three-digit number. The first digit indicated the company, the second indicated the platoon (0 for HQ, 1 for platoon, etc.), and the last number indicated the position of the tank within the platoon. There was a certain amount of variation in this system; for example, the platoon leader of the first platoon of the second company might be numbered either 210 or 211. In addition to this simple company system, there was also a numbering pattern for regimental and battalion command tanks. Regimental headquarters tanks usually used a two-digit number preceded by an 'R'; for example, R01 was the tank of the regimental commander, R02 was the executive officer. Similarly, the battalion headquarters used Roman numerals, with I for the first battalion, II for the second battalion, and so on; for example II01 would be the tank of the commander of the 2nd battalion. There were some variations in this system, with some regiments preferring the use of letters (A01, B01 instead of I01, II01), or further descriptors (RN1 for regimental radio). German heavy tank battalions (schwere Abteilung) sometimes used an S prefix for their three-digit code, and some flame-thrower and tank destroyer units were seen late in the war also using the S code (though for reasons that are not clear). In April 1944, the Inspector-General of the Panzerwaffe issued orders that formalized the numbering system, but added an important variation. Although most codes to date had been three-digit, AFVs other than tanks in regimental and battalion HQ companies were to use a four-digit number, the first two digits being arbitrarily assigned battalion or regimental code numbers. Therefore, the number 4203 would indicate the third AFV of a regiment using 42 as its code number. The code numbers were randomly assigned over the number 20, and some units such as armoured reconnaissance battalions were excluded. Besides the use of tactical numbering, some self-propelled artillery units instead used letters to identify batteries, on occasion qualified with a further number.

Tactical numbers varied enormously in style, size and location. Colouring usually depended on the background colour of the vehicle, with white and yellow lettering common on panzer grey vehicles. Some units used coloured numbers edged in white. The sequence of these colours, derived from the old bayonet knot system, were white, red, yellow, blue, light green and dark green (for an HQ vehicle). This system could be used at the discretion of unit commanders; for example, in the case of a panzer division with two panzer regiments and two panzer grenadier regiments, the four regiments would use the colours in the sequence mentioned, with divisional HQ using dark green. The system could also be used for smaller units; for example, to distinguish battalions within regiments. The extent to which the system was used is difficult to determine, and the description here is based on captured German records.

Although not strictly speaking a tactical numbering system, some German documents indicated that geometric signs could be used. The examples given were a diamond (1st battalion, or 1st company, etc.), a circle (2nd), a triangle (3rd) and a square (4th). This system does not appear to have been widely used after 1941, but there are photographs showing its employment with the 1., 2. and 11. Panzer Divisions to at least a limited extent during 'Barbarossa'.

Top left: Eight of these Pz Kpfw 1 Ausf Fs were sent to the Russian front with 1. Panzer Division in the summer of 1943, and this particular one, number 25, was captured intact by the Soviets. The tactical number is evident on the turret rear only, while to the left of the Balkan cross at the rear is a variation of the division's Berlin Bear insignia.

Centre left: Some Tiger battalions applied their turret tactical numbers in a unique fashion with the first (company) number noticeably larger than the platoon and vehicle number. This Tiger of sPzAbt 507, being inspected in 1945 by Soviet infantry after the vehicle had been disabled, shows the numbers painted over the track stowed on the turret side.

Bottom left: The Wehrmacht never indulged in naming vehicles to the same extent as the British or American armies, but this StuG III Ausf G has the name 'Sperber' painted in gothic lettering on the saukopf (boar's head cast) gun mantlet.

Top right: Camouflage schemes often were not uniformly applied in panzer divisions, as is evident in this view of two Hanomag Sd Kfz 251s of the Panzer Lehr Division in Budapest in 1944. The Sd Kfz 251 Ausf C on the right is elaborately finished with swaths of olive green and red-brown over the dark yellow base colour, while the Sd Kfz 251 Ausf D on the left has no disruptive pattern applied.

Below: When Italy left the Axis in 1943, many Italian units in Yugoslavia were rounded up by the Wehrmacht and their equipment impressed into German service. This AB 41 has been re-marked in German insignia, though, interestingly enough, the railroad loading label on the hull side incorrectly identifies the vehicle as an Sd Kfz 231. In the background is a 2cm FlaK 38 auf Fgst Zgkw 8t. Both vehicles appear to be finished in dark yellow overall but the AB 41 may still be Italian dark sand colour. These AB 41s were used extensively by anti-partisan units in Yugoslavia. (National Archives)

Above: Captured French Hotchkiss Char Leger H-39s were used extensively for anti-partisan duties in Yugoslavia, such as this vehicle serving with the 7. SS Freiwilligen-Gebirgs Division Prinz Eugen in Yugoslavia in 1944. Some captured French tanks retained their French Army green, but this vehicle appears to have been repainted in the standard German dark yellow. A white border-style Balkan cross is evident on the turret side, and below this on the hull is a typical railroad loading stencil in black. (National Archives)

Left: In 1945, German tanks began appearing in 'ambush pattern' camouflage, such as this Panther in Poland. This pattern consisted of the usual dark yellow with olive green and red-brown patterns, but the darker colours were broken up with a pattern of small speckles of the dark yellow colour, in an attempt at pointillistic disruption.

Right: A Panther finished in the 'ambush pattern' in action in Poland in 1945. In this case, the speckling patterns are quite varied, especially on the mantlet. This pattern was probably factory applied, or applied by specialist troops.

Below: Not all German armour in 1945 adopted the ambush schemes. Here, an old Panther Ausf D lies abandoned by the roadside in Poland. It is finished in the typical three-tone scheme.

Other Markings

Besides these tactical insignia, the German armed forces used a variety of other insignia or markings on their vehicles. German soft-skin vehicles, armoured cars and armoured half-tracks carried licence plates. On armoured vehicles, this consisted of a painted white rectangle with a thin black trim about 90mm high and 475mm long, centrally located on the bow with a six-digit number preceded by the arm of service code (WH–Wehrmacht, WL–Luftwaffe, SS–Waffen SS). The number was repeated on a rear plate, usually about 200mm high by 320mm wide. Often the rear number was painted on a conventional tin licence plate with clipped corners. The licence plates were sometimes stamped with a circular Feldpost number design with a German military eagle in the centre, but this marking was quite tiny. Although tanks and assault guns did not carry licence plates, on occasion the factory-applied chassis number could still be seen. Usually, it was painted over

for security reasons before the vehicle reached the troops.

One marking peculiar to the 'Barbarossa' operation and, in fact, a hold-over from the 1940 battle of France were the K (Kleist) and G (Guderian) letters painted on AFV mudguards of vehicles belonging to the panzer groups of these two generals. There were many other miscellaneous markings sometimes carried on German tanks and AFVs. 'Kill' markings traditionally were painted on gun tubes in the style of a thin white band. Names were occasionally painted on vehicles, and even cartoons, though this practice was certainly not as common as on British or American vehicles. More mundane markings, such as railroad loading labels or small stencilling for service notes, could also be seen. The stencilling instructions most commonplace were notes on wheeled vehicles indicating tyre pressure, and notes on the recuperator housings of tanks and assault guns referring to the use of an anti-freeze solution in the hydraulics (braun-ark).

German sales of tanks and assault guns to its Eastern European allies, 1940–44

	Bulgaria	Finland	Hungary	Romania	Slovakia
1940	37 Pz Kpfw 35(t)	–	–	–	–
1941	40 R-35	–	–	–	21 LT vz 40 32 Pz Kpfw 38(t)
1942	–	–	8 Pz Kpfw I 6 PzBfWg 102 Pz Kpfw 38(t) 32 Pz Kpfw IV 10 Pz Kpfw III	11 Pz Kpfw III 11 Pz Kpfw IV 26 Pz Kpfw 35(t)	–
1943	10 Pz Kpfw 38(t) 46 Pz Kpfw IV 25 StuG III 10 Pz Kpfw III 20 Sd Kfz 222, 223	30 StuG III	–	50 Pz Kpfw 38(t) 31 Pz Kpfw IV 4 StuG III	7 Pz Kpfw III 37 Pz Kpfw 38(t) 16 Pz Kpfw II 18 Marder II
1944	–	29 StuG III 15 Pz Kpfw IV 3 T-34	62 Pz Kpfw IV 5 Panther 3 Tiger I 40 StuG III 75 Hetzer	100 Pz Kpfw IV 114 StuG III	–

Below, top: In contrast to most German tanks, Royal Tigers often carried the Balkan cross insignia on the turret side rather than the hull. The cross on this Royal Tiger can be seen immediately above the black or red tactical number 311. This particular Royal Tiger and StuG III were knocked out during the fighting for the Sandomierz bridgehead south of Warsaw in August 1944. The Tiger probably belonged to sPzAbt 501, which was the first unit on the Eastern Front to be equipped with this behemoth.

Below, bottom: In the final days of the war, the two experimental Maus super-heavy tanks were sent into action, one near the proving grounds at Kummerdorf, the other at the approaches to OKH staff headquarters at Zossen. One was destroyed by its crew, while this one was captured by the Soviets. It is finished in dark yellow overall with a pattern of dark olive green and red-brown. It carries no unit insignia.

Soviet Union

The markings applied to Soviet armoured vehicles reflected the fortunes of war, as they did in the case of Germany. In the early years of the conflict, Soviet tanks, for security and other reasons, were marked very plainly, if at all. As the tide turned in 1942–43 the use of markings began to increase, owing in part to the formation of the new tank corps and the need for markings for logistics purposes. By war's end, the use of tactical markings on Soviet vehicles had reached its peak. Nevertheless, Soviet armoured vehicle markings were never applied as systematically as on German tanks. The Soviet Army was far more security conscious than the Wehrmacht, and there was not the same deep-rooted regimental tradition within the Red Army that fostered the sort of heraldic unit markings so popular in the Wehrmacht. As mentioned in the introduction, there has been no published Soviet study of military vehicle insignia of the Great Patriotic war and, therefore, many of the themes dealt with here can only be given tentative treatment until the Russians themselves begin to take an interest in the subject.

Camouflage Painting

Soviet Army vehicles traditionally have been finished only in dark olive green. The few actual samples of this that do remain show an extremely dark colour, almost a black-green, though conversations with veterans would seem to indicate that there was some variation in the shade, probably due to the enormous difficulties experienced by Soviet industry during the war.

During the 1939–40 Russo–Finnish War, all Soviet armoured vehicles initially were sent into action finished in dark green, even though the Karelian isthmus was already snow-covered. It was not until after the embarrassing defeats and the February–March 1940 counter-offensive that whitewash was issued for camouflage. As a result of the Finnish experiences, during the 1941–45 war Soviet armoured troops usually had available Type B paint, a water-soluble whitewash. In some cases this was issued directly to the troops but, as often as not, winter camouflage was applied by the remzavods (repair centres). It was scrubbed off in the spring. The usual style was to cover the whole vehicle with whitewash, though examples of speckled or mottled applications were seen occasionally.

There was little interest in pattern-painted camouflage, the emphasis in camouflage lectures being on the use of natural foliage when needed. Soviet quartermaster units had available brown, black and sand-grey paint on some occasions, but it was rarely used to camouflage tanks. A handful of Soviet tank units did use pattern-painted disruptive camouflage during the war, but this was exceedingly rare. For example, most of the 5th Guards Tank Corps was pattern-painted with brown swaths before the 1943 fighting around Kursk. The numerous accounts of

Below: The vast majority of Soviet tanks in service at the outbreak of war in June 1941 were unmarked. However, a number of vehicles of the 8th Mechanized Corps in the Ukraine were marked with small, white bands on the turret, such as this disabled BT-7 Model 1935 with three white stripes on the upper edge of its turret. These insignia may have been used to distinguish tank divisions within the corps. (National Archives)

Above: This disabled T-35 Model 1935 heavy tank of the 34th Tank Division, 8th Mechanized Corps is marked with two white bands on the upper turret, seen on a number of vehicles of this corps. (Ivan Bajtos)

Left: One of the most common forms of national identification markings used by the Soviet Army was the air identity marking painted on the turret roof. In the case of this T-26 Model 1933, a Cyrillic 'D' has been painted on the roof, the lower half being evident on the open turret hatches. This tank is being followed by an OT-130 flamethrower tank.

Right: A new T-34 Model 1941 disabled in the Karelian isthmus is inspected by Finnish troops in the autumn of 1941. (Note the hole in the bow.) This tank carries one of the earliest forms of the new tactical geometric markings, a rectangle containing the numbers 30/204. The meaning of the numbering is nearly impossible to decipher due to the innumerable variations in this type of marking. (Esa Muikku)

Below: A pair of T-28 medium tanks move into action in the autumn of 1941. The early rectangular tactical marking contains the number 3323, and is flanked by a solid white rectangle. These early war markings were often locally developed and non-standardized.

Above: A T-26 Model 1937 guards a street during the Soviet occupation of Tabriz, Iran, in September 1941. Many of the tanks and armoured cars used in this joint Anglo-Soviet venture were camouflaged with erratic patterns of sand paint over the usual dark green. In addition, all the armoured vehicles had a white cross painted on the turret roof for air identification. The white cross on the turret roof was the most common Soviet air identity marking, being used during pre-war manoeuvres, the 1940 occupation of the Baltic states, the 1941 invasion of Iran, and the April 1945 drive into Germany. Interestingly, it was also adopted during the 1968 invasion of Czechoslovakia. (Sovfoto)

Left: A T-26 Model 1937 and T-26 Model 1933 'sparrow shooter' advance towards the front during the defence of Moscow in November–December 1941. Both tanks are camouflaged with a hasty application of whitewash.

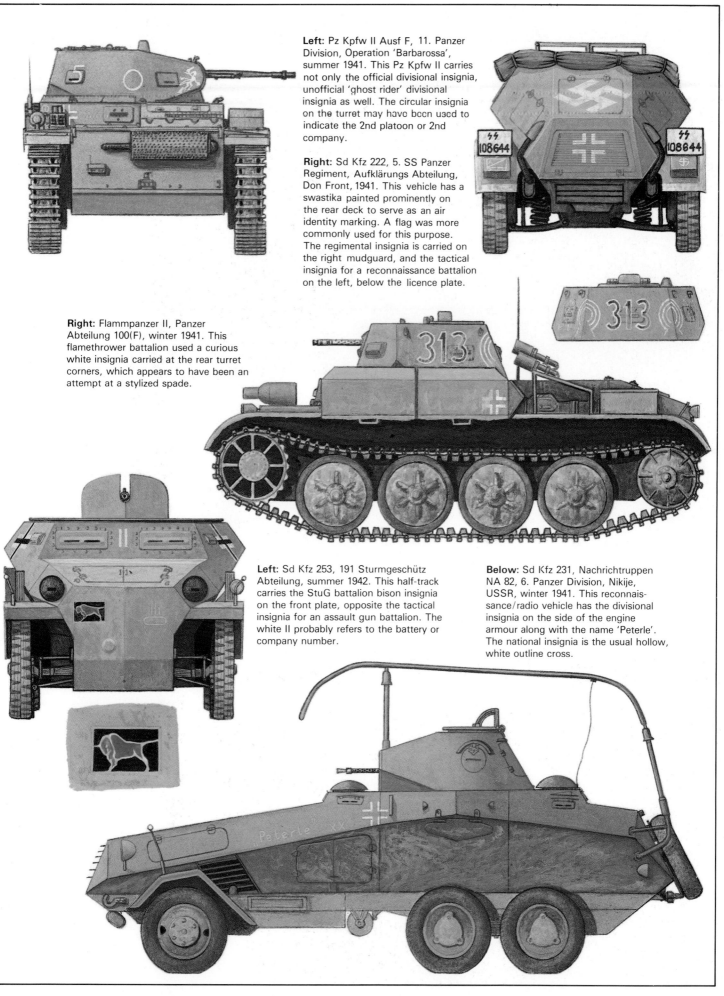

Left: Pz Kpfw II Ausf F, 11. Panzer Division, Operation 'Barbarossa', summer 1941. This Pz Kpfw II carries not only the official divisional insignia, unofficial 'ghost rider' divisional insignia as well. The circular insignia on the turret may have been used to indicate the 2nd platoon or 2nd company.

Right: Sd Kfz 222, 5. SS Panzer Regiment, Aufklärungs Abteilung, Don Front, 1941. This vehicle has a swastika painted prominently on the rear deck to serve as an air identity marking. A flag was more commonly used for this purpose. The regimental insignia is carried on the right mudguard, and the tactical insignia for a reconnaissance battalion on the left, below the licence plate.

Right: Flammpanzer II, Panzer Abteilung 100(F), winter 1941. This flamethrower battalion used a curious white insignia carried at the rear turret corners, which appears to have been an attempt at a stylized spade.

Left: Sd Kfz 253, 191 Sturmgeschütz Abteilung, summer 1942. This half-track carries the StuG battalion bison insignia on the front plate, opposite the tactical insignia for an assault gun battalion. The white II probably refers to the battery or company number.

Below: Sd Kfz 231, Nachrichtruppen NA 82, 6. Panzer Division, Nikije, USSR, winter 1941. This reconnaissance/radio vehicle has the divisional insignia on the side of the engine armour along with the name 'Peterle'. The national insignia is the usual hollow, white outline cross.

Left: During the defence of Moscow in 1941 some vehicles and artillery pieces were camouflaged in this intricate pattern of whitewash over the base dark green finish. Some green bands were left but were cross-hatched with white stripes. These T-34 Model 1941s probably belonged to the 11th Tank Brigade. (Sovfoto)

unpainted Soviet tanks being rushed from the factories is attributable to journalistic licence. By 1942, when most of these reports were filed, the Soviet factories had been evacuated to the Urals. The only case where this might have happened to a limited extent was during the battle at Stalingrad in autumn 1942, when the STZ tank factory was still located within the city.

National Insignia

The traditional insignia of Soviet Russia has been the red star. Although this was used on parade tanks or for public display before the war, it was not used regularly as a means of national identification. It was applied occasionally by crews on an unofficial basis during the course of the war, and its use increased dramatically in the final year of the war. However, even then it was far from commonplace. Occasionally, the hammer and sickle emblem was used, but this was more for decorative purposes than as a proclamation of national identity.

The most common form of national identity insignia used by the Soviet Army was, in fact, air identity markings. The usual national identity markings are a hindrance; if they are large and serve their function they tend to make excellent aiming points for enemy anti-tank gunners, but if they are small and inconspicuous they do not fulfil their purpose of identifying the tank to friend or foe. In any event, ground troops soon come to recognize friendly and enemy tanks by their shape and sound. The real problem comes from aircraft, since aircrews are notorious in nearly all armies for not being able to distinguish between friendly and hostile tank columns. In 1934, the Soviet Army began using a large white cross painted on the roof of tank turrets to serve as a means of identifying them as friendly vehicles. This marking was used regularly in summer wargames. There were other attempts to use large letters so that observation aircraft could distinguish one brigade from another. During the occupation of the Baltic states in 1940, Soviet tanks used the white cross insignia on their roofs, and even as late as 1941 when the Germans invaded Russia some of these tanks still had this marking.

As the war continued, the Soviet Army adopted other similar insignia. These air identity markings were changed frequently to prevent the Germans from recognizing them and trying to confuse Soviet Shturmovik (ground-attack) aircraft by painting their own panzers with similar insignia. Usually, such a marking would be adopted immediately before a major offensive and applied at the last minute to maintain security. Very few of these insignia have been identified positively since aerial views of Soviet tanks are so uncommon. Some insignia known to have been used were a white triangle with red star, a white triangle with yellow circle, a white band extending from side to side of the turret (1943), a red band running over the vehicle from front to rear (Hungary, 1944), and a white circle (Baltic campaign, 1944, and Yugoslavia, 1945). The best known of these markings was the white cross and white turret band used at the time of the Berlin operation in 1945. In early 1945, during joint Allied discussions, the United States suggested that the Soviet Union, Britain and the US should agree to a set of tank markings to reduce the risk of inadvertent calamaties when both sides met in Germany and to prevent American aircraft from attacking Soviet columns, as had been happening in Yugoslavia. The Soviets suggested that Soviet tanks should have a single white band painted around the tank turret, and the United States and Britain should use two white bands. The US backed down, preferring to continue to use the fluorescent red and yellow air identity panels that were already in use with US, British, French and other Allied forces. Nevertheless, the committee agreed that, as of April 1945, the air recognition sign for Soviet vehicles would be a white cross on the turret roof and a white band around the turret sides. This was put into effect, though its application was not universal. However, in April, the Wehrmacht demonstrated that they understood the system; and American fighter-bomber pilots complained that they had spotted German armoured formations painted with Soviet air identification bands. As a result, the Soviets agreed that, as of 1 May, they would switch from a turret cross to a white triangle. However, the war ended before this was put into widespread use, and the only evidence of its application comes from a few photographs of vehicles in Prague after the May ceasefire.

Right: A platoon of disabled OT-133 flamethrower tanks show another variation of the geometric tactical insignia used by Soviet tank units. In this case, the numbers in the centre of the triangle presumably indicate the individual vehicle and platoon (13 on the left and 12 on the right) while the 2/4 on the left and right indicate the battalion and company respectively. (Iván Bajtos)

Centre right: Soviet units occasionally used captured German tanks, such as this unit employing a Pz Kpfw IV Ausf D marked with a communist hammer and sickle to distinguish it from its German kin. (George Balin)

Bottom right: Some Soviet tank units used letters rather than numbers to distinguish their vehicles, such as this KV-1 Model 1941 with a Cyrillic 'G' on the turret sides and rear. This vehicle is camouflaged in bands of dark green and field-brown. (George Balin)

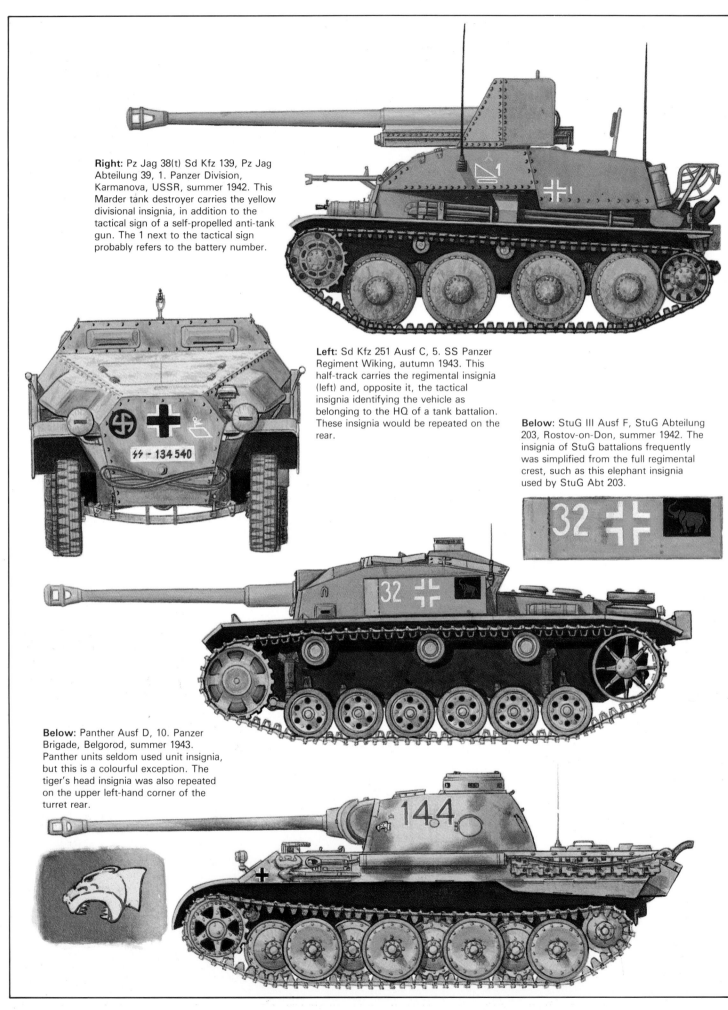

Right: Pz Jag 38(t) Sd Kfz 139, Pz Jag Abteilung 39, 1. Panzer Division, Karmanova, USSR, summer 1942. This Marder tank destroyer carries the yellow divisional insignia, in addition to the tactical sign of a self-propelled anti-tank gun. The 1 next to the tactical sign probably refers to the battery number.

Left: Sd Kfz 251 Ausf C, 5. SS Panzer Regiment Wiking, autumn 1943. This half-track carries the regimental insignia (left) and, opposite it, the tactical insignia identifying the vehicle as belonging to the HQ of a tank battalion. These insignia would be repeated on the rear.

Below: StuG III Ausf F, StuG Abteilung 203, Rostov-on-Don, summer 1942. The insignia of StuG battalions frequently was simplified from the full regimental crest, such as this elephant insignia used by StuG Abt 203.

Below: Panther Ausf D, 10. Panzer Brigade, Belgorod, summer 1943. Panther units seldom used unit insignia, but this is a colourful exception. The tiger's head insignia was also repeated on the upper left-hand corner of the turret rear.

Left: Pz Kpfw III Ausf N, Panzer Regiment 3, 2. Panzer Division, Kursk, 1943. Besides the usual white trident insignia, tanks of this unit had their own regimental insignia carried on the turret sides. The three-digit tactical number was only carried on the rear of the turret armour.

Right: Sd Kfz 131 Marder II, summer 1943. This vehicle carries one of the less-common style of Balkan crosses used in 1943. It is also unusual in that its tactical number is quite small and inconspicuous.

Above: Tiger I, sPzAbt 505, eastern Poland, summer 1944. Curiously, some Tigers of this battalion had a patch of Zimmerit stripped clean on which was painted the battalion insignia. Another oddity was the use of the gun tube for carrying the battalion insignia.

Left: Ferdinand, Pz Jag Regiment 656, Nikopol bridgehead, Donets River Front, November 1943. Some vehicles of this regiment appear to have adopted a tiger's head insignia after the battle at Kursk; this was carried on the glacis plate.

Left: Some tanks had the names of heroes painted on their side, such as this BT-5 Model 1934 with the name 'Zoya Kosmodemyanskaya', a young partisan who was killed by the Germans in 1941. Below the name is written the town 'Irkutsk', and a tactical number is carried on the turret front.

Centre left: Another style of tactical numbering used during the war was a mix of letters and numbers, such as on this BA-10 armoured car with 'I-36'.

Bottom left: In 1942, the Soviet Army began using brigade insignia, as witnessed on this Lend-Lease M3 Lee tank. Usually within a tank corps, each of the three tank brigades would have a common design with a variation to distinguish between them. (Sovfoto)

Top right: Many Lend-Lease vehicles, such as this Universal Carrier, retained the leftovers of their previous owner's markings; note the British serial number here. The Russian script behind it is a shipping instruction applied in Britain, beginning with the word 'Attention'. This vehicle also has white bumper markings, the significance of which is not known. (Sovfoto)

Bottom right: Soviet tankers on their Lend-Lease M3A1 (diesel) light tanks are armed, equipped and attired in American gear. The tanks were marked in a style common in 1942 and 1943, with the number '58' probably being a brigade code, and the number after it the individual vehicle number. (Sovfoto)

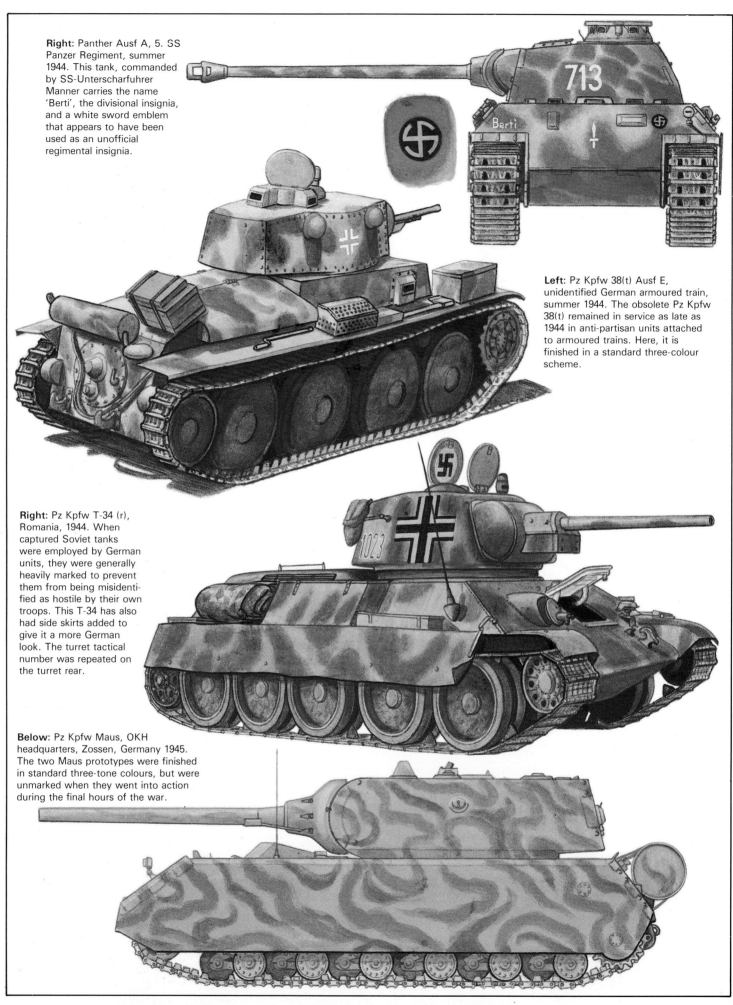

Right: Panther Ausf A, 5. SS Panzer Regiment, summer 1944. This tank, commanded by SS-Unterscharfuhrer Manner carries the name 'Berti', the divisional insignia, and a white sword emblem that appears to have been used as an unofficial regimental insignia.

Left: Pz Kpfw 38(t) Ausf E, unidentified German armoured train, summer 1944. The obsolete Pz Kpfw 38(t) remained in service as late as 1944 in anti-partisan units attached to armoured trains. Here, it is finished in a standard three-colour scheme.

Right: Pz Kpfw T-34 (r), Romania, 1944. When captured Soviet tanks were employed by German units, they were generally heavily marked to prevent them from being misidentified as hostile by their own troops. This T-34 has also had side skirts added to give it a more German look. The turret tactical number was repeated on the turret rear.

Below: Pz Kpfw Maus, OKH headquarters, Zossen, Germany 1945. The two Maus prototypes were finished in standard three-tone colours, but were unmarked when they went into action during the final hours of the war.

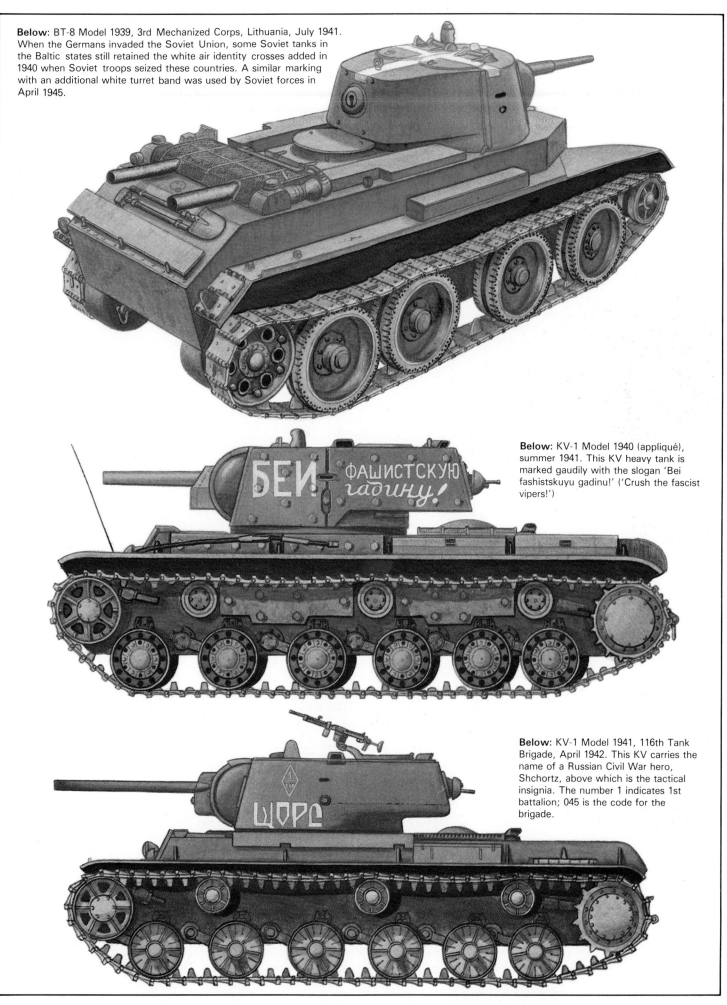

Below: BT-8 Model 1939, 3rd Mechanized Corps, Lithuania, July 1941. When the Germans invaded the Soviet Union, some Soviet tanks in the Baltic states still retained the white air identity crosses added in 1940 when Soviet troops seized these countries. A similar marking with an additional white turret band was used by Soviet forces in April 1945.

Below: KV-1 Model 1940 (appliqué), summer 1941. This KV heavy tank is marked gaudily with the slogan 'Bei fashistskuyu gadinu!' ('Crush the fascist vipers!')

Below: KV-1 Model 1941, 116th Tank Brigade, April 1942. This KV carries the name of a Russian Civil War hero, Shchortz, above which is the tactical insignia. The number 1 indicates 1st battalion; 045 is the code for the brigade.

Left: Although application of pattern-painted camouflage during the summer months was not common on Soviet vehicles, whitewash camouflage was de rigeur during the winter. There was seldom any care taken with these whitewash applications, but in the case of this BA-10 the finish has been applied in a distinct pattern.

Below left: Soviet tanks and armoured vehicles were not commonly camouflaged with pattern-painted disruptive schemes, but such camouflage was commonplace on armoured trains due to their vulnerability to air attack. Trains were commonly camouflaged in dark green with field-brown or light green swaths.

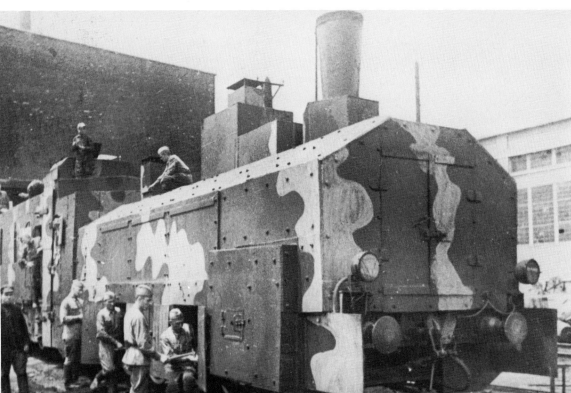

Tactical Insignia

Starting in 1931, Soviet tanks began to use a complicated set of red, white and black bands to distinguish battalions and companies. The top band indicated the battalion, and the bottom, dotted band indicated the company. The colour sequence was red (1st battalion or company), white (2nd battalion or company) and black (3rd battalion or company). Platoon and vehicle were indicated by a number in a small square which was painted on the hull side. The battalion and company bands were painted on the upper edge of the turret. This system fell into disuse from 1938 onwards, and it was no longer in use by the outbreak of war, even though some older tanks could still be seen in these markings well into 1941 and 1942. During the opening phases of the war, the Soviet Army's vehicles were nearly totally devoid of markings. This was due in no small measure to the confusion surrounding the formation of the new mechanized corps in 1940–41. Gradually, a new style of marking began to develop that was in many respects similar to the German tactical map symbols.

Vehicles began to have geometric shapes painted on their turrets, with numbers carried within the marking. It is not known whether there was any system to these shapes, as was the case in the British Army, but a range of shapes have been observed in photographs of the 1941–42 period: squares, rectangles, diamonds, triangles and circles. These may have been part of an abortive marking scheme for the new tank corps of 1942. In any event, the system seems to have disappeared by the time of the fighting in summer 1943, leaving only one common survivor, the diamond tank marking. The diamond was an obvious choice of marking, since it was the Soviet Army map symbol for a tank. Use of this marking began in 1942, and the marking was usually applied to the turret, about 400mm high in white or yellow paint. The diamond contained two sets of numbers stacked one above the other. The initial pattern appears to have been that the brigade number appeared on the bottom and the battalion number on top. Brigades at this stage in the war were usually given coded numbers, so for a tank of the 1st Battalion, 116th Tank Brigade, the number appeared as 1/045; 045 was the brigade code. This symbol remained in use to the end of the war, but the numbering system within it varied enormously. In some cases the brigade number was not coded and would be carried on the top rather than the bottom. Therefore, the symbol of the 2nd Company, 3rd Battalion, 44th Tank Brigade appeared as 44/32. Sometimes the battalions were indicated by a letter rather than a number. The usual sequence for this (in Cyrillic) was A, B, V. When the lettering system was used, the battalion number usually appeared at the top of the diamond. Later in the war, when the Red Army began to use brigade and corps insignia, there was no pressing need for the diamond system to carry information on the brigade, so the numbering often referred instead to battalion, company and platoon. In short, there was very little consistency in the use of the symbol and it is frequently impossible to decipher one from the other without further information. The consequent confusion was probably intentional, since it made it very difficult for the Germans to gather intelligence data from Russian tank wrecks. This system was the most common form of tactical insignia used by Soviet tanks, but its use was far from universal. Besides the diamond, late in the war other symbols were also employed, especially the square. This contained the same sort of numbered information, but was usually divided into three or four segments with up to four sets of numbers. This system appears to have been most common on self-propelled guns, but it was seen on tanks, armoured cars and other vehicles as well. The significance of the use of a square rather than a diamond is not known. A number of tactical insignia are shown in the illustrations and photographs here.

New geometric insignia designs began to appear on Soviet tanks beginning late in 1942. These sometimes resembled the tactical insignia mentioned above, but were in fact a new type of marking, the corps insignia, and their evolution is discussed below. It is sometimes very difficult to distinguish between these two categories, since some units, such as the 23rd Tank Corps, used the traditional diamond insignia for their brigades in the same way as the tactical markings described above.

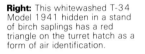

Right: This whitewashed T-34 Model 1941 hidden in a stand of birch saplings has a red triangle on the turret hatch as a form of air identification.

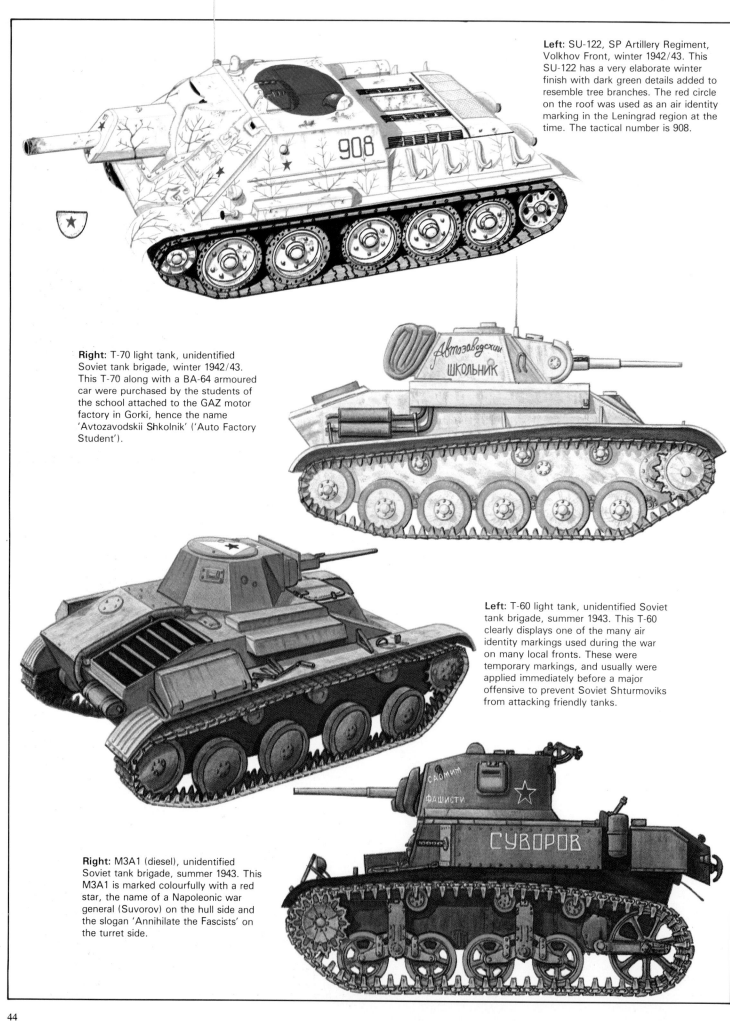

Left: SU-122, SP Artillery Regiment, Volkhov Front, winter 1942/43. This SU-122 has a very elaborate winter finish with dark green details added to resemble tree branches. The red circle on the roof was used as an air identity marking in the Leningrad region at the time. The tactical number is 908.

Right: T-70 light tank, unidentified Soviet tank brigade, winter 1942/43. This T-70 along with a BA-64 armoured car were purchased by the students of the school attached to the GAZ motor factory in Gorki, hence the name 'Avtozavodskii Shkolnik' ('Auto Factory Student').

Left: T-60 light tank, unidentified Soviet tank brigade, summer 1943. This T-60 clearly displays one of the many air identity markings used during the war on many local fronts. These were temporary markings, and usually were applied immediately before a major offensive to prevent Soviet Shturmoviks from attacking friendly tanks.

Right: M3A1 (diesel), unidentified Soviet tank brigade, summer 1943. This M3A1 is marked colourfully with a red star, the name of a Napoleonic war general (Suvorov) on the hull side and the slogan 'Annihilate the Fascists' on the turret side.

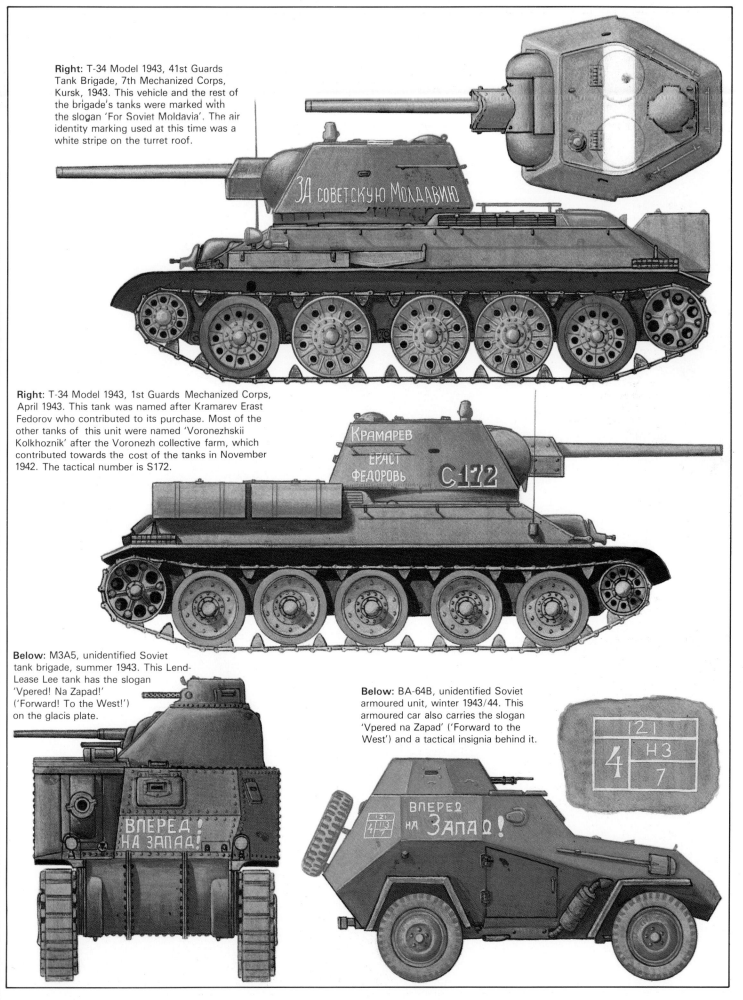

Right: T-34 Model 1943, 41st Guards Tank Brigade, 7th Mechanized Corps, Kursk, 1943. This vehicle and the rest of the brigade's tanks were marked with the slogan 'For Soviet Moldavia'. The air identity marking used at this time was a white stripe on the turret roof.

Right: T-34 Model 1943, 1st Guards Mechanized Corps, April 1943. This tank was named after Kramarev Erast Fedorov who contributed to its purchase. Most of the other tanks of this unit were named 'Voronezhskii Kolkhoznik' after the Voronezh collective farm, which contributed towards the cost of the tanks in November 1942. The tactical number is S172.

Below: M3A5, unidentified Soviet tank brigade, summer 1943. This Lend-Lease Lee tank has the slogan 'Vpered! Na Zapad!' ('Forward! To the West!') on the glacis plate.

Below: BA-64B, unidentified Soviet armoured unit, winter 1943/44. This armoured car also carries the slogan 'Vpered na Zapad' ('Forward to the West') and a tactical insignia behind it.

Top left: One of the most common forms of slogan was the commemorative slogan which referred to the collectives or youth groups that contributed money to the construction of a column of tanks. In the case here, a whitewashed T-34 Model 1943 has had the name 'Khabarovskii Komsomolyots' added in red on the turret. This refers to the Young Communist League of the city of Khabarovsk.

Below left: These KV-1 Model 1941s at one time were perhaps finished uniformly in whitewash, but by the time this photograph was taken in the winter of 1942/43 the whitewash had been worn away on the engine deck, exposing the original dark green finish. On the turret side and rear are three-digit tactical numbers in red or black.

Top right: Some of the new brigade insignia that began to appear in 1942 were extremely complex, as is evident on this T-60. One of the other brigades of this corps used a similar marking, but with an additional crescent above the '3'.

Centre right: This is believed to be a T-34 Model 1943 of the 22nd Tank Brigade, 6th Tank Corps. The number in the diamond is 22/14, the first half indicating brigade, the second indicating vehicle number. There is one stripe on the bulged trunnion housing on the turret front, possibly indicating the 22nd Tank Brigade, which was the first of three brigades in the corps. The two stripes between the 14 on the turret rear may indicate the 2nd battalion of the brigade.

Bottom right: A pair of BA-10 armoured cars of a reconnaissance battalion in Schlüsselburg, February 1943. They carry both a three-digit turret number as well as a triangular unit insignia in red on the turret sides and rear. (Sovfoto)

German Unit Insignia

Panzer Divisions

1 2 3 4 5 6 7 8 9 10
11 12 13 14 15 16 17 18 19 20
21 22 23 24 25 26 27 28 29 30
31 32 33 34 35 36 37 38 39 40
41 42 43 44 45 46 47 48 49 50

SS Panzer Divisions

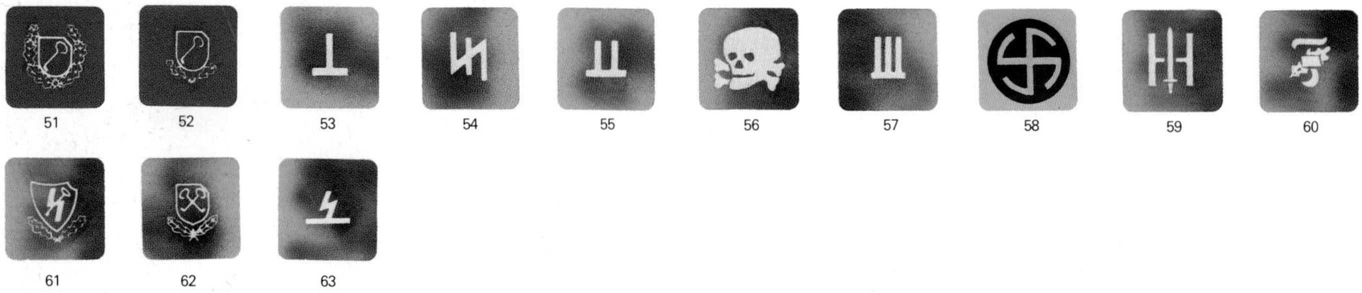
51 52 53 54 55 56 57 58 59 60
61 62 63

Sturmgeschutz Units

64 65 66 67 68 69 70 71 72 73
74 75 76 77 78 79 80 81 82 83
84 85 86 87 88 89 90 91 92 93
94 95 96 97 98 99

Right: A column of T-34 Model 1943 advance in the summer of 1943. They carry a white air identity triangle on the roof. The leading vehicle is numbered 25-14, a numbering style that was commonplace during the 1942–43 period, with the first two digits often being coded brigade designators. (Sovfoto)

Below: T-34 Model 1942s and Model 1943s are presented to the crews of the Estonian 45. uksik tanki polk in May 1943, part of the 8th Estonian Infantry Corps. The tanks are decorated with the slogan 'For Soviet Estonia', which is painted in Russian on top and in Estonian below. This was one of the Soviet Army's two Estonian tank regiments formed during the war. (Sovfoto)

GERMAN UNIT INSIGNIA

German Panzer Divisions
1, 1. Pz Div, 1940–45
2, 1. Pz Div, 1941–42
3, 2. Pz Div, 1940–43
4, 2. Pz Div, 1943–45
5, 2. Pz Div (coy insignia)
6, 2. Pz Div (coy insignia)
7, 3. Pz Div
8, 3. Pz Div (unofficial)
9, Pz Rgt 6 (3. Pz Div)
10, 4. Pz Div
11, 5. Pz Div
12, 5. Pz Div
13, Pz Rgt 31 (5. Pz Div)
14, 6. Pz Div
15, 6. Pz Div (temporary, Sept–Oct 1941)
16, 6. Pz Div (temporary, 1943)
17, 7. Pz Div

18, 7. Pz Div (temporary)
19, 8. Pz Div
20, 9. Pz Div
21, 10. Pz Div
22, Pz Rgt 7 (10. Pz Div)
23, 11. Pz Div
24, 11. Pz Div (unofficial)
25, 12. Pz Div
26, 13. Pz Div
27, 14. Pz Div
28, 16. Pz Div
29, 17. Pz Div
30, 18. Pz Div
31, 18. Pz Bde (18. Pz Div)
32, 19. Pz Div
33, 20. Pz Div (to 1941)
34, 20. Pz Div, 1941–45
35, 22. Pz Div
36, 23. Pz Div
37, 23. Pz Div (unofficial)

38, 24. Pz Div
39, 24. Pz Div, 1943–45
40, 25. Pz Div
41, 25. Pz Div
42, 27. Pz Div
43, 27. Pz Div (alternate)
44, 28. Pz Div
45, Pz Lehr Div
46, Pz Lehr Div
47, Pz Rgt Stab, Fall Pz Div Hermann Göring
48, 1 Kp, Pz Rgt, Fall Pz Div Hermann Göring
49, Fall Pz Div Hermann Göring (unofficial)
50, 10. Pz Bde

SS Panzer Divisions
51, 1. SS Pz Div Leibstandarte Adolf Hitler

52, 1. SS Pz Div Leibstandarte Adolf Hitler
53, 1. SS Pz Div Leibstandarte Adolf Hitler, 1943
54, 2. SS Pz Div Das Reich
55, 2. SS Pz Div, 1943
56, 3. SS Pz Div Totenkopf
57, 3. SS Pz Div Totenkopf, 1943
58, 5. SS Pz Div Wiking
59, 9. SS Pz Div Hohenstaufen
60, 10. SS Pz Div Frundsberg
61, 12. SS Pz Div Hitler Jugend
62, 1. SS Pz Kp
63, General Komm SS-Pz Kp, 1943

Sturmgeschütz Units
64, StuG Abt 177

65, StuG Abt 184
66, StuG Abt 185
67, StuG Abt 189
68, StuG Abt 190
69, StuG Abt 191
70, StuG Abt 197
71, StuG Bde 201
72, StuG Bde 202
73, StuG Bde 203
74, StuG Bde 209
75, StuG Abt 210
76, StuG Abt 226
77, StuG Bde 232
78, StuG Bde 236
79, StuG Bde 237
80, StuG Bde 243
81, StuG Bde 245
82, StuG Bde 249
83, StuG Bde 259
84, StuG Bde 261

85, StuG Bde 277
86, StuG Bde 278
87, StuG Bde 279
88, StuG Bde 286
89, StuG Bde 287
90, StuG Bde 301
91, StuG Bde 322
92, StuG Bde 341
93, StuG Bde 393
94, StuG Bde 666
95, StuG Bde 667
96, StuG Bde 901
97, StuG Bde 912
98, StuG Bde Grossdeutschland
99, StuG Bde Pz Lehr

Left: An M3A1 (diesel), marked with the town name 'Kuibyshev' and the rare red star marking. National stars of this sort were not commonly used on Soviet tanks during the war until 1945. Faintly visible is the vehicle's original US War Department serial in blue drab paint: U.S.A. W. 307216.

Below left: This whitewashed Churchill Mk III was named 'Alexander Nevskii' after the legendary prince who defeated the Teutonic knights. It has the Guards insignia on the front of the turret, on either side of the gun. Nevskii was a very popular name for tanks during the war, no doubt due to the attention paid to his exploits in the Eisenstein film that was so popular during the war years. (George Balin)

Below: The tank crews of the 30th Guards Tank Brigade pose in front of a T-34 Model 43 near Leningrad after having been decorated. The tank carries a red star and the marking 'Stalinetz', in front of which is the Order of the Red Banner. Barely evident is a pattern of field drab paint over the basic dark green colour. The 30th Guards Tank Brigade was originally a light tank brigade fighting in the Leningrad area on T-60 light tanks. After this photograph was taken the brigade was reorganized again with IS-2 heavy tanks and fought in the Baltic and East Prussian campaigns in 1944–45. (Sovfoto)

Unit Insignia

The mechanized corps of the Soviet Union in 1941 do not appear to have used any divisional insignia. The only exception appears to have been the 8th Mechanized Corps in the Ukraine; several photographs of tanks believed to belong to this unit show small white bars painted on the turret sides, which may have distinguished the divisions within this corps. The mechanized corps were disbanded in the wake of the 1941 disaster and replaced in 1942 with the new tank corps and mechanized corps. It should be kept in mind that these later corps were in fact divisional-sized formations, contrary to their Soviet misnomer. A tank corps consisted of three tank brigades and one mechanized brigade plus support units, while a mechanized corps had three mechanized brigades and one tank brigade. Each mechanized brigade had a tank regiment, so these units in fact had more tanks than a panzer division during the later stages of the war and were much better equipped than their German counterpart, the panzer grenadier divisions. The new formations did not make use of divisional insignia to any great extent until 1944 during the great offensives through central Europe. By this time, divisional insignia were introduced for logistical reasons to ease the task of the military police; often it became necessary for them to direct tank columns from different units and these insignia saved them having to ask each crew which unit they served with. Divisional insignia were issued by the staffs of Fronts (equivalent to Western Armies), and often were only temporary. They were not always applied to tanks and from some unit histories it is evident that they were used mainly as road markers.

There is no comprehensive listing of these markings available, and what little has been gathered comes mainly from careful perusal of Soviet unit histories, photographs and German intelligence reports. Usually, a corps would employ a simple device with a letter or other symbol distinguishing brigades. For example, during Operation 'Bagration' in 1944, the 2nd Guards Tank Corps was assigned the use of a white arrow. Above the arrow was painted one of three letters (Cyrillic L, B or I), which indicated 4th Guards Tank Brigade, 25th Guards Tank Brigade and 26th Guards Tank Brigade respectively. Under this was painted a three-digit vehicle tactical number, being issued in the 100, 200 and 300 block for each of the three brigades. The 11th Guards Tank Corps simply used white bars during their drive through south-eastern Europe into Yugoslavia in 1945. These small bars, about 200mm in length, were painted on the front of the turret sides; one bar for 40th Guards Tank Brigade, two bars for 44th Guards Tank Brigade and three bars for 45th Guards Tank Brigade. Interestingly enough, this unit also retained the older style map tactical insignia which was explained above. Other similar systems are shown in the illustrations and photographs. One of the more unique styles was used by the 4th Guards Mechanized Corps. It consisted of animal symbols for each of its brigades: a bear, donkey, rhino and running dog. Some independent regiments were also given insignia, particularly heavy tank (IS-2) and self-propelled gun regiments, several of which are shown in the accompanying illustrations. These markings were usually painted in white, though on occasion they were painted in yellow. On white, snow finishes they were painted in red or black.

Top left: Although dedication markings were usually painted in white on tanks, on these KV-1 Model 1941s, the marking 'Moskovskii Osoaviakhimovyets' was applied in red. This slogan refers to the Moscow branch of the League for Air and Chemical Defence, which contributed funds for the purchase of the tanks.

Below left: A T-34-85 Model 1944 of the 25th Guards Tank Brigade, 2nd Guards Tank Corps disabled in fighting in East Prussia in January 1945. This corps used a white arrow as the corps insignia with a letter above it indicating the brigade, in this case a Cyrillic B for the 25th Guards Tank Brigade.

Top right: A rear view of an SU-76 Suka SP gun clearly showing a very intricate regimental insignia. The two bars and three triangles probably were used to distinguish the companies and batteries of this regiment. Above it is the six-digit serial unique to SU-76 guns. Few other Soviet armoured vehicles had their serial numbers painted externally. (Sovfoto)

Below right: A battery of SU-76 Sukas of the First Byelorussian Front advance in eastern Germany in February 1945. The splotch winter camouflage pattern is fairly unique for Soviet vehicles. (Sovfoto)

Patriotic Slogans

Probably the best known style of tank marking used on Soviet combat vehicles during the Great Patriotic War was the patriotic marking. In fact, the term patriotic marking is something of a misnomer, as there were several categories of large slogans painted on Soviet vehicles during the war. In much the same way that heraldic vehicle symbols are rooted in German culture, the large painted slogans can be traced back to Russian culture in both the form of religious banners and, in Soviet Russia, to political banners. Originally, these slogans were probably prompted by the proselytizing of unit political commissars, but there can be little doubt that the practice eventually became more spontaneous. The early slogans are reminiscent of turgid Communist tracts, such as 'Stamp out the nests of the Fascist Vipers', and 'For Stalin!'. This style continued through the war in similar forms, such as 'For 20 Years of Soviet Rule in Uzbekistan', 'For the Soviet Ukraine', but it was

joined eventually by less dogmatically inspired sentiments such as 'Onward to Riga!', 'Onward to the West', 'To Berlin', 'Kill the Fascist Occupiers'.

There were two other distinct categories of such markings: dedication slogans, and popular heroes' names. Indeed, dedication slogans were probably the most common form of large written marking to appear on Soviet tanks during the war. As in the US and British war bond drives, Soviet workers were encouraged (somewhat forcibly at times) to donate money for the purchase of weapons. During the war, 5.8 billion rubles was donated for the purchase of over 30,000 armoured vehicles amounting to about one third of total production. Usually, a small ceremony would be held in which representatives of the collective farm (Kholkoz) or factory group would hand over the tanks to their new crews. Often these tanks were marked with the name of the collective, or with an appropriate slogan. Therefore, whole brigades would be named 'Moscow Kholkoz', or

Left: Captured German equipment was usually clearly marked to prevent misidentification. This StuG III, which is still in its German dark yellow finish, has no less than three red stars as well as the slogan 'Smert Nemyetskii Okkupanta' ('Death to the German Occupiers'). The vehicle took part in the attack on Melitopol. (Sovfoto)

Below: An ISU-152 during the final drive on Berlin in the spring of 1945 displays a regimental or brigade insignia on the hull front, a tactical number, and the marking 'Osvobozhdennaya Kirovskaya' ('Liberated Kirovskaya') on the side.

'Khabarovsky Young Communist League', for example. Sometimes these markings were applied only in chalk and would be removed before the troops entered combat, but in some cases the markings were more permanent. It is difficult to estimate how many Soviet tanks were marked in this fashion, but it was probably no more than about 1 per cent.

Another popular style of marking was the commemoration of some Russian hero by painting his name on tanks. Among the most popular names were the medieval princes Dmitri Donskoi and Aleksander Nevskii, both known for their wars against foreign invaders. Other popular names were Shchortz (a Civil War general), and generals from the Napoleonic period, such as Suvorov. On some occasions, the tanks would be named after soldiers who had been killed in the fighting.

During the war, particularly in the later phases, the Soviet government took great pains to justify its rule over some of the more recalcitrant ethnic minorities of the USSR. The new acquisitions on the Baltic coast were of special concern. As a result, some tanks appeared in action with slogans other than Russian. One Churchill tank brigade carried the slogan 'For the Soviet Ukraine' in Ukrainian; the Estonian 45th Tallin Tank Regiment (45. uksik tanki polk) carried the slogan 'For Soviet Estonia' in both Russian and Estonian; and the 51st Tank Regiment (51. uksik tanki polk) was named after the legendary Estonian hero Lembitu, though in this case, written in Cyrillic. Latvian crews of the 6th Mechanized Brigade named their T-34 Model 1943 tanks 'Latvian Rifles' in Latvian. One of the more novel markings, for which, unfortunately, only a written description exists, was the use of the Russian Orthodox cross on a T-34 brigade. This stemmed from the fact that the brigade was one of a number purchased by donations from the Orthodox Church through the sale of its precious religious vessels.

Right: An M4A2 (76mm) outside Gdansk in January 1945. It is displaying insignia believed to be that of the 64th Guards Tank Regiment. Behind the insignia is the tactical number 216, indicating the 2nd battalion, 1st company. Within each ten-tank company, the company commander would use 0, the first platoon 1–3, the second 4–6 and the third 7–9, which would make this a tank of the 2nd platoon.

Below: A Soviet armoured column halts in the ruins of Favoritstrasse in Vienna, April 1945. The M4A2 (76mm) is followed by two Universal Carriers, which have the brigade insignia (a small swallow) on the hull side and on the rear. No markings are evident on the Sherman tank. (Sovfoto)

Below: A pair of SU-76M Sukas move up on the outskirts of Vienna in April 1945. The vehicle nearest the camera has the name 'Kalinniets' painted on the side, while the vehicle in front has the serial 412047 and the yellow tactical number 125 on the rear access door. (Sovfoto)

Right: A battery of SU-85s enter Bucharest, Romania in the summer of 1944. The tactical number is S-13 (the S being the Cyrillic S, which resembles the Roman C). The S probably indicated the fourth battery of a tank destroyer battalion. (Sovfoto)

КАЛИНИНЕЦ

Left: An SU-57 (T-48 57mm Gun Motor Carriage) of the Soviet tank destroyer brigade moves through the streets of Prague in May 1945. The brigade's insignia is a yellow diamond with the number '36' inside. The white tactical number is repeated on the hull side and rear. Although not evident in this view, other photographs of the vehicles of this unit indicate that it was one of the few Soviet units to carry the proper air identity marking for May 1945, a white triangle on the front engine deck. (Sovfoto)

Centre left: A platoon of T-34-85 Model 1945s advance on Berlin. The vehicle nearest the camera is carrying the appropriate slogan 'Vpered na Berlin!' ('Onward to Berlin!').

Bottom left: A column of T-34-85 Model 1944 advance through East Prussia in February 1945. The tactical number 1200 is undoubtedly that of the company commander, 2nd company, 1st battalion of a tank brigade. The writing on the turret side reads 'For Soviet Uzbekistan!'.

Tactical Numbering

The Soviets did not use a standard system of tactical vehicle numbering during the Second World War. This was due in part to security concerns, but also because until 1943 not all Soviet tanks carried radios. The primary reason for the use of large tactical numbering on turrets is to facilitate inter-vehicle communication, but the absence of radios in all but platoon and company commander's tanks until 1942–43 meant that this style of marking was of little use. When receivers were finally issued, numbers began to appear with some frequency. The style of these numbers varied enormously. While the Germans mainly used three-digit numbers, Soviet tanks used one-, two-, three- and four-digit numbers, numbers and letters, numbers broken with hyphens and a bewildering assortment of styles. Initially, the style appears to have been a direct transfer from the numbering in the same tactical diamond insignia mentioned earlier, but with a hyphen in place of the upper/lower position used in the diamond. Therefore, instead of 45/15 (a brigade coded 45, 1st battalion, 5th platoon), the number simply became 45-15. Similarly, in a diamond using letters to indicate battalions, the diamond was dropped and the tactical numbering instead became A-01, K-40, etc. This style was supplanted eventually by two- and three-digit numbers without hyphens or letters in 1944 and 1945. The meaning of the numbers varied from unit to unit. In the 1st Guards Mechanized Corps, a three-digit number was used. The first number indicated the brigade, and the second and third were issued to all 65 tanks of the brigade consecutively. Therefore, tank 104 belonged to the 1st Guards Mechanized Brigade, 231 belonged to the 2nd Guards Mechanized Brigade and 323 belonged to the 3rd Guards Mechanized Brigade. A related system was used by the 18th Tank Corps. The first digit represented the brigade, and the numbers used were 4, 5 and 6 for the 110th, 170th and 181st Tank Brigades respectively. In other units, a more complicated system

was used. The first digit indicated the battalion, the second identified the company and the third indicated the platoon and vehicle. Soviet tank battalions during this period had a single battalion HQ tank, plus two companies each with ten tanks (1 company command tank, three platoons of three tanks each). Therefore, 100 was the battalion command tank, 110 was the command tank of the first company, 111 was the command tank of the 1st platoon, 1st company, 114 was the command tank of the 2nd platoon, 1st company, etc. This system could be expanded to four numbers, in which case the first number indicated the brigade within a tank corps. These notes can only scratch the surface of the enormous variation in Soviet tank numbering during the war, because of the enormous variety of systems and the many inconsistencies in practical use. One type of numbering not commonly seen on Soviet armoured vehicles was the vehicle serial number. The only vehicle on which this was seen regularly was the SU-76, which had a five- or six-digit number carried on the front and rear of the fighting compartment.

Other Markings

The Soviet Army usually did not indicate 'kill' markings on tanks or other vehicles. On the rare occasions when 'kill' markings were carried, the style depended on the crew. Some crews placed small, white stars on the turret sides, others put silhouettes on the gun barrel or small X marks. On vehicles received through Lend-Lease, the Soviets usually left the vehicles in their original colours with their original markings. These included packing and moving instructions, serial numbers, inspection markings and a host of other small stencilling. Both British and American serial numbers usually were left intact. In fact, the 'USA' serials on American vehicles and tanks became so commonplace in Eastern Europe in 1944 that local folk wisdom held it to be an acronym of 'Ubiyat Sukinsyna Adolfa' ('Kill that son-of-a-bitch Adolf')!

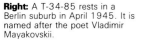

Right: A T-34-85 rests in a Berlin suburb in April 1945. It is named after the poet Vladimir Mayakovskii.

Above: The T-34-85 Model 1944 of Lieutenant I. G. Goncharenko, Hero of the Soviet Union, in Prague, May 1945. It carries the tactical number 1–24. This vehicle belonged to the 63rd Guards Tank Brigade, 10th Guards Tank Corps, as is evident from its brigade insignia below the number. The two other brigades of this corps had one or two strokes in the design instead of three as is the case here. Goncharenko's tank is often mistakenly identified as number 1–23 and, in fact, the memorial to Goncharenko in Prague is not only mistakenly numbered, but is an IS-2 instead of a T-34-85. (CTK via Jiri Hornat)

Left: A T-34-85 tank from the 44th Guards Tank Brigade, 11th Guards Tank Corps in Yugoslavia in 1945. Tanks of the 11th Guards Tank Corps had small dashes on the turret front: one dash indicated the 40th, two the 44th and three the 45th Guards Tank Brigade. The tactical diamond insignia also contains the brigade number as well as the vehicle number (38) below.

Above right: With the ruined Reichstag in the background, Soviet troops are addressed by their commander before returning

to the Soviet Union on 20 May 1945. The BA-64B armoured car is decorated gaudily for the occasion with the slogan 'Slava Stalinu' ('Glory to Stalin') on the front, and 'Kavkaz-Berlin' ('Caucasus-Berlin') on the side. (Sovfoto)

Centre right: An IS-2m heavy tank enters Hradec Kralove in north-eastern Bohemia, Czechoslovakia in early May 1945. Its tactical number is 1–12, which in a heavy tank regiment would indicate 1st company, 1st platoon, 2nd vehicle. (CTK via Jiri Hornat)

Below right: An IS-2m heavy tank prowls the streets of Berlin in April 1945. It is marked very clearly with the white turret band and white roof cross, which were adopted by the Soviet Army in April 1945 to prevent its tanks from being engaged mistakenly by American or British tanks and aircraft approaching Soviet lines from the west. The breaks in the turret band are probably explained by the fact that this was a reserve tank of the 85th Heavy Tank Regiment and it had not yet had the regimental insignia (a white boar on a red star) or the tactical number painted on, both of which would have been positioned in the gaps.

Bulgaria

Bulgaria was allied to Germany during the war on the Eastern Front, but refused to declare war on the Soviet Union. It joined the war in 1941, allowing German troops transit to Greece and itself occupying territory in that country, including Macedonia. Eventually, it sent troops to Yugoslavia where they were engaged in anti-partisan duties to keep open the Belgrade–Greece roads. The Bulgarian armoured force initially consisted of eight Vickers 6-ton tanks acquired in 1938 and fourteen Italian CV 33 tankettes acquired in 1934. These were used to form two tank companies in the two rapid divisions. In February 1940, the Germans supplied the Bulgarian Army with 36 Pz Kpfw 35(t)s. In June 1941, the Bulgarians consolidated their very limited armour resources into the 1st Armoured Brigade, which comprised the 1st Tank Regiment and the 1st Mechanized Infantry Regiment. The tank regiment nominally consisted of a reconnaissance company with the fourteen CV 33 tankettes, and two tank battalions, one of Pz Kpfw 35(t) and the Vickers, plus another equipped with 40 French R-35s donated by the Germans. This unit saw no significant fighting and its equipment was clearly outdated. The Germans finally consented to modernize it, and beginning in July 1943 supplied Bulgaria with 46 Pz Kpfw IVs, 10 Pz Kpfw IIIs and 25 StuG III assault guns, 20 Sd Kfz 222 armoured cars, and necessary howitzers, anti-tank guns and other equipment. The newly rejuvenated tank regiment was supposed to consist of three battalions, each with two companies of 15 Pz Kpfw IVs and a company of Pz Kpfw 35(t) or 38 (t) for a total of 140 tanks, but its strength never reached this level. This was probably just as well for the Wehrmacht, as on 9 September 1944 Bulgaria switched sides and turned on its former ally. The 1st Armoured Brigade served alongside Soviet units and took part in the fighting in Hungary in 1945.

Bulgarian armour, from what little evidence is available, carried no national markings until 1943. The Vickers, Pz 35(t) and CV 33s remained in the camouflage schemes of their manufacturers with only a Bulgarian Army licence number added. These licence numbers consisted of a thin white rectangle about 450mm long in which was painted a five-digit number preceded by the Cyrillic letter V (similar to the Roman B) for Voiska (Army). The Pz 35(t) tanks had two-digit turret tactical numbers painted on. In 1943, when the new German equipment began to arrive, the 1st Armoured Brigade adopted the same insignia carried by Bulgarian aircraft up to that time, a white square with black X, about 500mm high. In September 1944 the Tsar was overthrown and the Tsarist insignia was dropped as a consequence. The Army substituted a shield in the national colours of white, green and red, which was painted on some tanks both in the form of a small shield added to the licence plate in front of the number and as a large turret marking. Some Pz Kpfw IVs had the shield painted on the turret schürzen side screens. The few photographs that do exist would seem to indicate that Bulgarian StuG IIIs remained in their original German dark yellow paint. However, it would appear that the Pz Kpfw IVs were repainted in dark green overall.

Above: A column of Bulgarian Pz Kpfw IVs of the 1st Armoured Brigade in operation against the Germans near Nagykanizsa on 2 April 1945. The insignia of the insurgent, anti-Tsarist forces was the national shield in white/red/green, as seen on the turret of the leading tank. (Ivan Bajtos)

Below: Although it would appear that Bulgarian Pz Kpfw IVs were repainted in dark green, Bulgarian StuG IIIs such as this vehicle in action in Hungary in 1945 appear to have been left in German dark sand. This vehicle still retains the Tsarist insignia, a black X on a white square, carried on the centre of the schürzen spaced armour. (Ivan Bajtos)

Croatia

After the fall of Yugoslavia in 1941, the Germans formed a Croatian puppet state under Ante Pavelić. The state had no formal armour units as far as is known, but was supplied with a small number of Italian and ex-Hungarian CV 33 and CV 35 tankettes which were used for anti-partisan duty. Later, H-39 Hotchkiss light tanks about one-company strong were supplied for the same role. The tankettes were marked with the state's crest, a red and white chequer-board shield, which was contained within a large white U, the U being a reference to the Ustashi Fascist movement. This insignia was carried on the glacis plate. The H-39s apparently were not marked, and at least one photograph indicates that they retained their original German Balkan cross insignia.

Czechoslovakia

Left: Lieutenant A. Sochor, I. Bruzik and Lieutenant R. Tesarik of the 1st Czechoslovak Tank Regiment pose in front of Tesarik's tank, 'Lidice', after they had received the decoration 'Hero of the Soviet Union' in June 1944. The name on the T-34 Model 43 is in the later, small style and refers to the Czech village massacred by the Germans in reprisal for the assassination of Heydrich. When first formed, many of the tanks of the regiment carried names such as this covering the whole turret.

In June 1943 the Czechoslovak Independent Brigade was formed in the Soviet Union with an attached tank battalion. It was equipped with T-34 Model 43s, T-70 light tanks and BA-64B armoured cars. It took part in the fighting around Kiev, and in April 1944 was expanded into the 1st Czechoslovak Tank Regiment, with two battalions. Finally, in the summer of 1944 another battalion was added, which became the 1st Czechoslovak Tank Brigade. The unit was organized along Soviet lines and fought during the Carpathian battles, ending the war in Prague. At this stage it was equipped with T-34-85s, and had small numbers of other vehicle types, including a few IS-2 heavy tanks.

Initially, the unit carried no national markings. Instead, the tanks were named after Czech towns, legendary figures from Czech history and so on, which were painted on the vehicles in large letters. Among the names and towns used were Jan Zizka, Otakar Jaros, Janosik, Lidice, Lezaky, Sokolova, Praha, Podkarpatsky Partyzan and others. The lettering was very large initially, about 900mm high, but eventually it was reduced in size to about 350mm. The name was usually carried on the upper forward edge of the tank turret. In 1945, when the brigade was finally fighting on Czechoslovak soil, the standard national blue/white/red roundel was used for national identification, usually positioned on the front sides of the turret. At this time, tactical numbering was also added behind the national roundel. The numbering was usually three-digit, and eventually was preceded by the letters CS, the abbreviation for Czechoslovak. These tanks sometimes also carried a small bisected circle insignia, which was probably the Soviet-style brigade insignia.

Besides these regular tank units, during the Prague uprising in 1945 the Czech insurgents captured large numbers of German armoured vehicles, especially Hetzers. Many of these were marked with large chalked slogans or national identification symbols.

Left: A column of T-34-85s of the 1st Czechoslovak Tank Brigade enters Prague in May 1945. Besides their three-digit tactical number, the national tricolour is evident on the turret front. (CTK via Jiri Hornat)

Panzer Grenadier Divisions
100, 3. Pz Gren Div
101, 4. SS-Polizei Pz Gren Div
102, 10. Pz Gren Div
103, 11. SS Pz Gren Div Nordland
104, 11. SS Pz Gren Div Nordland
105, 16. Pz Gren Div
106, 16. SS Pz Gren Div Reichsfuhrer
107, 17. SS Pz Gren Div Gotz von Berlichigen
108, 18. Pz Gren Div
109, 18. Pz Gren Div Horst Wessel
110, 20. Pz Gren Div
111, 25. Pz Gren Div
112, 28. SS Pz Gren Div Wallonien
113, 29. Pz Gren Div
114, 38. SS Pz Gren Div Nibelungen
115, 60. Pz Gren Div
116, Pz Gren Div Feldherrnhalle
117, Pz Gren Div Grossdeutschland

Schwere Panzer Abteilung Insignia
118, sPzAbt 501
119, sPzAbt 502
120, sPzAbt 503
121, sPzAbt 504
122, sPzAbt 505
123, sPzAbt 506
124, sPzAbt 506
125, sPzAbt 507
126, sPzAbt 508
127, sPzAbt 509
128, 8. sPzKp, 2. SS Pz Rgt

SOVIET UNIT INSIGNIA
129, 3rd Tk Bde (23rd Tk Cp)
130, 4th Gds Tk Bde (2nd Gds Tk Cp)

131, 4th Gds Tk Cp
132, 25th Gds Tk Bde (2nd Gds Tk Cp)
133, 26th Gds Tk Bde (2nd Gds Tk Cp)
134, 36th Gds Tk Bde (4th Gds Mech Cp)
135, 37th Gds Tk Rgt (15th Gds Mech Bde, 4th Gds Mech Cp)
136, 38th Gds Tk Rgt (13th Gds Mech Bde, 4th Gds Mech Cp)
137, 39th Gds Tk Rgt (14th Gds Mech Bde, 4th Gds Mech Cp)
138, 39th Tk Bde (23rd Tk Cp)
139, 40th Gds Tk Bde (11th Gds Tk Cp)
140, 41st Gds Tk Bde (7th Mech Cp)
141, 44th Gds Tk Bde (11th Gds Tk Cp)
142, 45th Gds Tk Bde (11th Gds Tk Cp)
143, 51st Tk Bde (3rd Tk Cp)
144, 54th Gds Tk Bde (7th Gds Tk Cp)
145, 55th Gds Tk Bde (7th Gds Tk Cp)
146, 56th Gds Tk Bde (7th Gds Tk Cp)
147, 58th Tk Rgt (16th Mech Bde, 7th Mech Cp)
148, 60th Mech Bde (4th Mech Cp)
149, 62nd Gds Tk Bde (10th Gds Tk Cp)
150, 63rd Gds Tk Bde (10th Gds Tk Cp)
151, 64th Gds Tk Rgt (8th Gds Mech Cp)
152, 78th Hvy Tk Rgt
153, 84th Tk Rgt (63rd Mech Bde, 7th Mech Cp)
154, 85th Hvy Tk Rgt
155, 95th Tk Bde (9th Tk Cp)

156, 135th Tk Bde (23rd Tk Cp)
157, 177th Tk Rgt (64th Mech Bde, 7th Mech Cp)
158, 366th Gds Hvy SP Arty Rgt
159, 1219th SP Arty Rgt
160, 1443rd SP Arty Rgt
161, Unidentified tk bde (T-34 Mod 43, summer 1943)
162, Unidentified tk bde (T-34-85, 1945)
163, Unidentified tk unit (T-34 Mod 43, summer 1944)
164, Unidentified tk rgt (M4A2, summer 1944)
165, Unidentified tk bde (T-34 Mod 43, summer 1944)
166, Unidentified tk unit (M3A5, summer 1943)
167, Unidentified tk bde (T-34-85, M4A2 (76mm), 1945)
168, Unidentified tk bde (T-70, KV-1, summer 1943)
169, Unidentified tk unit (M4A2 (76mm), Bren Carrier, 1945)
170, Unidentified tk bde (T-34 Mod 43, 1943)
171, Unidentified hvy tk rgt (IS-2, 1945)
172, Unidentified SP arty rgt (SU-76, 1944–45)
173, Unidentified SP arty rgt (SU-85, 1944–45)
174, Unidentified hvy SP arty rgt (ISU-152, 1945)
175, Tac mkg, 2nd Btn, 116th Tk Bde, 1942
176, Tak mkg, CO's tank, 2nd Pl, 2nd Coy, 3rd Btn (V), 51st Tk Rgt
177, Unidentified tk destroyer bde (SU-57, 1945)
178, Unidentified tk unit (T-34 Mod 43, 1943)

179, Unidentified tk unit (T-34 Mod 43, 1943)
180, Tac mkg, unidentified tk unit (T-34 Mod 41, 1942)
181, Tac mkg, 109th Tk Bde, 16th Tk Cp (T-34 Mod 43, 1944)
182, Tac mkg, 4th Bty, 17th veh, 1202nd SP Arty Rgt SU-85, 1944)
183, Tac mkg, unidentified tk unit (T-34-85, 1945)
184, Tac mkg, unidentified tk unit (T-34-85, 1945)
185, Tac mkg, unidentified tk unit (T-34 Mod 41, 1942)
186, Tac mkg, unidentified tk unit (Valentine, 1943)
187, Tac mkg, unidentified tk unit (Valentine, 1943)
188, Tac mkg, unidentified tk unit (OT-26, 1942)
189, Tac mkg, unidentified armd unit (BA-10, 1942)
190, Air identity mkg (T-60, 1943)
191, Air identity mkg (T-34 Mod 43, 1943)
192, Guards insignia
193, Order of Red Banner insignia

POLISH UNIT INSIGNIA
194, Polish national insignia, mkg of 1st Polish Armd Bde
195, 2nd Polish Armd Bde, 4th Polish Armd Bde, 1st Polish Armd Cp
196, 16th Polish Ind Armd Bde
197, 3rd Polish Armd Bde, (1st Polish Armd Cp)
198, 4th Polish Hvy TK Rgt

CZECHOSLOVAK UNIT INSIGNIA
199, Czech national insignia, 1945

200, 1st Czechoslovak Tk Bde, 1945

FINNISH UNIT INSIGNIA
201, Finnish hakaristi national insignia, 1942–45

ROMANIAN UNIT INSIGNIA
202, Romanian national insignia
203, Romanian national insignia (air identity)
204, Romanian national insignia (variation on light-coloured camouflage)

BULGARIAN UNIT INSIGNIA
205, Bulgarian national insignia, 1941–44 (Tsarist)
206, Bulgarian national insignia, 1944–45 (communist)

SLOVAK UNIT INSIGNIA
207, Slovak national insignia
208, Slovak national crest

HUNGARIAN UNIT INSIGNIA
209, Hungarian national crest
210, Hungarian national insignia, 1941
211, Hungarian national insignia, 1942–45
212, 1st Hungarian Cav Div
213, Unidentified Hungarian Turan tk unit
214, 2nd Hungarian Armd Div
215, Ludovika Academy armd vehicles
216, Csaba unit, 2nd Hungarian Armd Div
217, Light tk coy
218, Medium tk coy
219, Heavy tk coy
220, Late-style Hungarian serial number

German: Panzer Grenadier Divisions

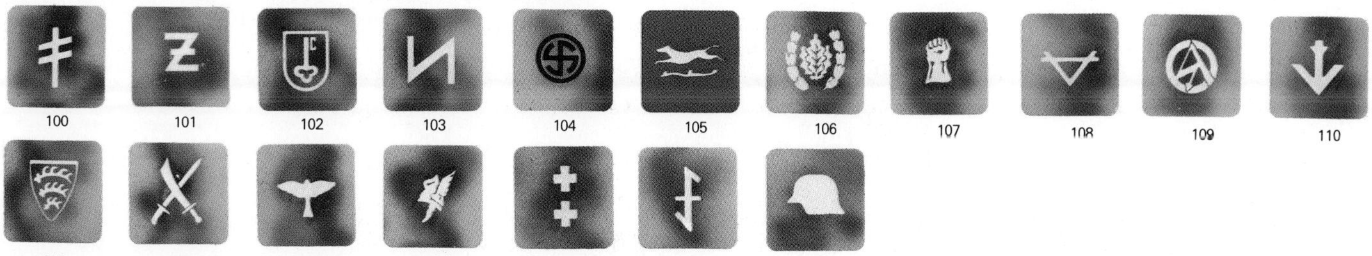

100 101 102 103 104 105 106 107 108 109 110
111 112 113 114 115 116 117

German: Schwere Panzer Abteilung

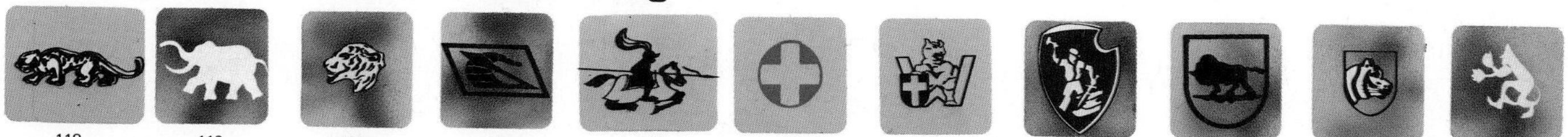

118 119 120 121 122 123 124 125 126 127 128

Soviet Unit Insignia

129 130 131 132 133 134 135 136 137 138 139
140 141 142 143 144 145 146 147 148 149 150
151 152 153 154 155 156 157 158 159 160 161
162 163 164 165 166 167 168 169 170 171 172
173 174 175 176 177 178 179 180 181 182 183
184 185 186 187 188 189 190 191 192 193

Polish, Czechoslovak, Finnish, Romanian, Bulgarian, Slovak and Hungarian Insignia

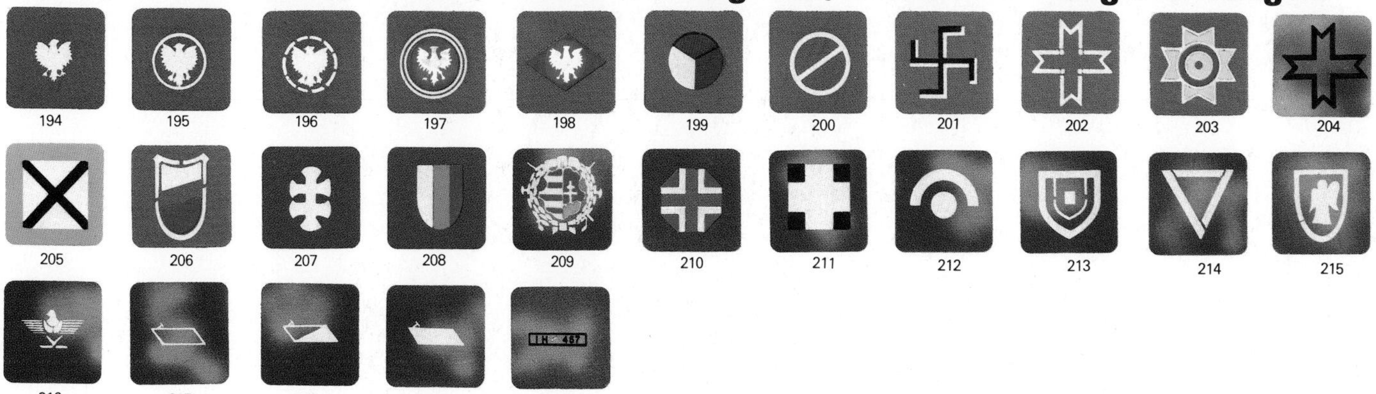

194 195 196 197 198 199 200 201 202 203 204
205 206 207 208 209 210 211 212 213 214 215
216 217 218 219 220

Above: An IS-2m of the 1st Czechoslovak Army Corps enters the Old Town section of Prague in May 1945. The national flag is flown from the roof, and the tricolour insignia carried on Czechoslovak armour is very evident on the turret front. (CTK via Jiri Hornat)

Centre left: A French AMR 35 captured from the Germans by Czech insurgents in the 1945 Prague uprising is still finished in German three-tone camouflage, but has CSR chalked on its side and front as a form of national identification. (CTK via Jiri Hornat)

Bottom left: During the Prague uprising, the Czech insurgents seized a number of uncompleted Hetzer tank destroyers at their factory. This particular vehicle had the missing gun mantlet port plated over and an MG42 machine-gun put in its place. A shield was also added around the machine-gun on the roof. The slogan on the side skirt reads 'Smrt nemeckym vrahum' ('Death to the German Murderers'). (CTK via Jiri Hornat)

Finland

During the 1939–40 Winter War, the Finnish Army fielded a single tank battalion formed in December 1939 with two companies of obsolete FT-17s, two companies of Vickers 6-ton tanks and a former tank replenishment company. The first armoured unit to see action was a squadron of Landsverk 182 armoured cars of the Cavalry Brigade, though in January 1940 this unit was reformed as the 6th Tank Company. Of the tank companies, only the 4th Tank Company saw much fighting, losing seven of its thirteen Vickers plus two damaged. Although this small force did not play a major role in the 1940 war, large numbers of Soviet tanks were destroyed or captured and were used to form the basis for new armoured units raised in 1940–41. The Tank Battalion was considerably strengthened and modernized, having three tank companies, a heavy tank platoon and three armoured car platoons. As of 31 May 1941, the Finnish Army had 11 BA-20, 10 BA-10, 1 Landsverk

182, 29 T-37, 13 T-38, 26 T-26E (these were Vickers 6-ton tanks with Soviet 45mm guns added, not Soviet-built T-26s), 10 T-26 Model 1931, 20 T-26 Model 1933, 4 T-26 Model 1937, 2 T-28, 2 OT-26, 4 OT-130, 62 Komsomolets, 1 Vickers M 1933, 1 Vickers Mk III and 4 FT-17. On 10 February 1942, the tank force was reorganized into an expanded Tank Brigade consisting of the 1st Tank Battalion with the 1st, 2nd and 3rd Tank Companies, and the 2nd Tank Battalion with the 4th and 5th Tank Companies and the understrength Heavy Tank Company. Each company but the last had three platoons with five tanks each plus a company command tank. Finally, in June 1942 the Armoured Division was organized with the Tank Brigade, the 1st Infantry Brigade and support units. Finnish tank units fought from the outset of the Continuation War on 26 June 1941. By 1943, it was becoming apparent that much of its equipment was obsolescent, which led to the

Below: This ex-Soviet OT-130 flamethrower tank has had the Finnish national insignia added to the turret in the form of white/pale blue/white turret bands. This insignia remained in use from 1940–41, but gave way to the far less conspicuous hakaristi insignia before the outbreak of the 1941 war. (National Archives)

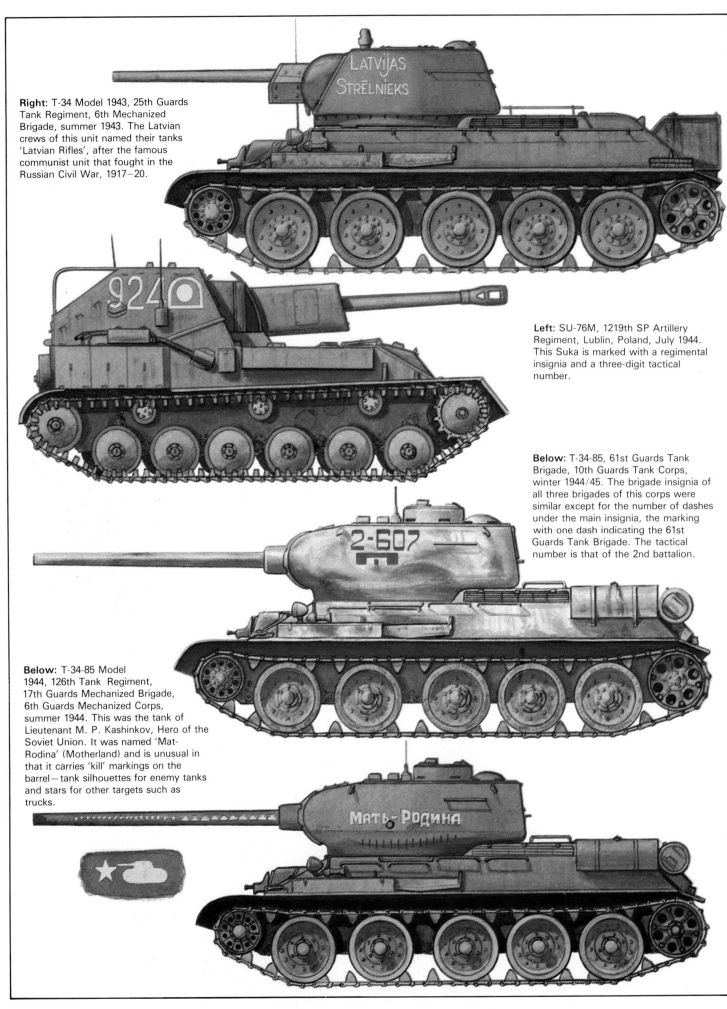

Right: T-34 Model 1943, 25th Guards Tank Regiment, 6th Mechanized Brigade, summer 1943. The Latvian crews of this unit named their tanks 'Latvian Rifles', after the famous communist unit that fought in the Russian Civil War, 1917–20.

Left: SU-76M, 1219th SP Artillery Regiment, Lublin, Poland, July 1944. This Suka is marked with a regimental insignia and a three-digit tactical number.

Below: T-34-85, 61st Guards Tank Brigade, 10th Guards Tank Corps, winter 1944/45. The brigade insignia of all three brigades of this corps were similar except for the number of dashes under the main insignia, the marking with one dash indicating the 61st Guards Tank Brigade. The tactical number is that of the 2nd battalion.

Below: T-34-85 Model 1944, 126th Tank Regiment, 17th Guards Mechanized Brigade, 6th Guards Mechanized Corps, summer 1944. This was the tank of Lieutenant M. P. Kashinkov, Hero of the Soviet Union. It was named 'Mat-Rodina' (Motherland) and is unusual in that it carries 'kill' markings on the barrel—tank silhouettes for enemy tanks and stars for other targets such as trucks.

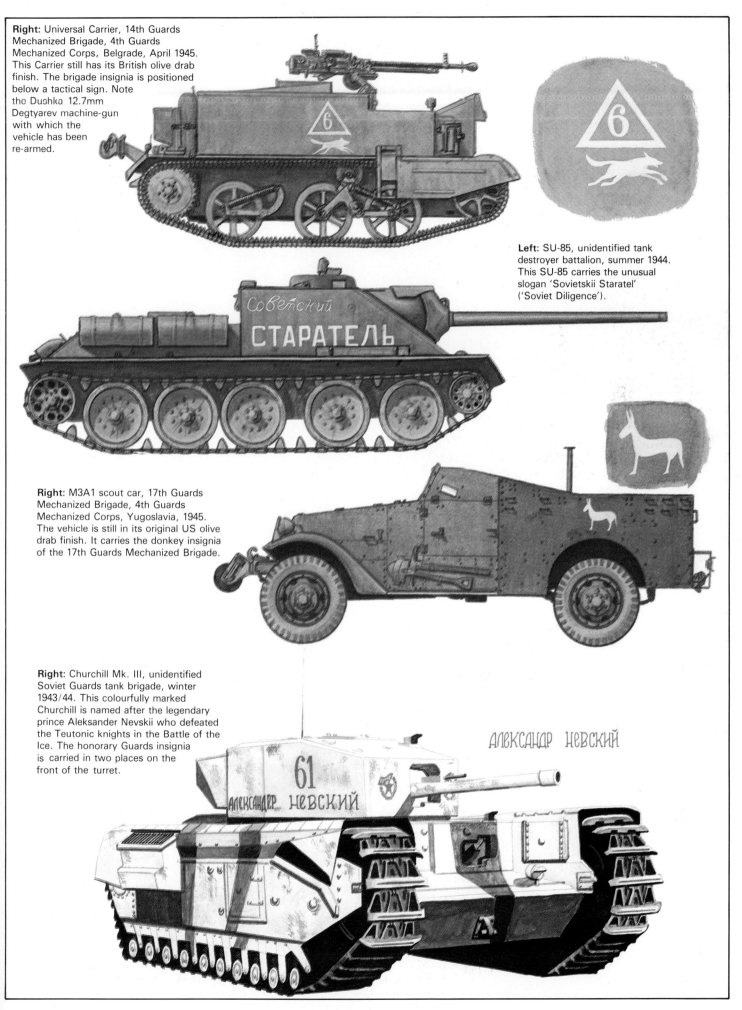

Right: Universal Carrier, 14th Guards Mechanized Brigade, 4th Guards Mechanized Corps, Belgrade, April 1945. This Carrier still has its British olive drab finish. The brigade insignia is positioned below a tactical sign. Note the Dushka 12.7mm Degtyarev machine-gun with which the vehicle has been re-armed.

Left: SU-85, unidentified tank destroyer battalion, summer 1944. This SU-85 carries the unusual slogan 'Sovietskii Staratel' ('Soviet Diligence').

Right: M3A1 scout car, 17th Guards Mechanized Brigade, 4th Guards Mechanized Corps, Yugoslavia, 1945. The vehicle is still in its original US olive drab finish. It carries the donkey insignia of the 17th Guards Mechanized Brigade.

Right: Churchill Mk. III, unidentified Soviet Guards tank brigade, winter 1943/44. This colourfully marked Churchill is named after the legendary prince Aleksander Nevskii who defeated the Teutonic knights in the Battle of the Ice. The honorary Guards insignia is carried in two places on the front of the turret.

Советский СТАРАТЕЛЬ

АЛЕКСАНДР НЕВСКИЙ

61 Александр Невский

Left: This Vickers of the 4th Independent Tank Company was knocked out by the Russians during the 1940 winter war. It is fitted with a 37mm Bofors gun. Although badly burned, the remains of white/pale blue/white turret bands are still faintly visible on the turret sides.

Centre left: This T-28 at Keskuskorjaamo, Hameenlinna in the spring of 1940 is finished in white overall with pale blue bands to simulate shadows, a pattern adapted from the style used on Finnish artillery. (Esa Muikku)

Bottom left: A parade by T-26 Model 1931 vehicles of the 2nd Tank Company, Finnish Tank Battalion in 1941. On the turret of the left tank can be seen the early full-armed hakaristi. The 'R-numbers' (76, 77) are clearly evident on both vehicles and close inspection of the glacis of the left tank near the light will reveal the dragon insignia sometimes used by this unit.

Right: A T-50 of the Heavy Tank Company, Tank Brigade in the spring of 1942. This vehicle's 'R-number', 110, is obscured by the mudguard support, but parts of it can be seen on the upper right edge of the glacis plate. The later short-arm hakaristi are quite clear in this view. (Esa Muikku)

Bottom right: A T-26 Model 1937 of the 3rd Tank Company in the summer of 1944. This vehicle is finished in the three-tone camouflage scheme of grey, moss green and sand brown. It carries a three-digit tactical number in yellow (315). (Esa Muikku)

purchase of 6 Landsverk Anti 40mm SP guns from Sweden and 30 StuG IIIs from Germany. The Landsverks were used by the Armoured AA Battery of the Armoured Division, while the StuG IIIs were used to re-equip the Assault Gun Battalion, which had previously used the BT-42. The BT-42 was a Finnish improvisation built in 1942 and consisted of a First World War-vintage British 114mm howitzer mounted on a captured Soviet BT-7 chassis. In June 1944, the Soviets launched a major counter-offensive against Finland to eliminate that country from the war. During the savage fighting that summer it became evident that more modern equipment was desperately needed, leading to the purchase of 29 StuG III, 15 Pz Kpfw IV and 3 T-34 from Germany. The Finns signed an armistice on 4 September 1944. In the following months of the Lappland War, when German troops were forced to withdraw, the tanks played little active role.

Tanks in the 1940 Winter War were finished in dark green overall. Their turrets were painted with white/pale blue/white bands (the national colours) to distinguish the Vickers from the very similar Soviet T-26. This form of national insignia remained in use in 1940, but on 21 June 1941 the hakaristi was adopted as the new tank insignia. This marking bears no relation to the Nazi swastika, having been used on Finnish aircraft since 1918. The orders showed a short-arm version of this insignia, but initially the troops painted on a black insignia with white shading that had full-length arms like the aircraft insignia. Only later did the official, short-armed version become prevalent. During the winter months of the Continuation War, Finnish tanks were finished in white. In the spring of 1943, the summer scheme of dark green overall was superceded by a three-colour camouflage scheme of moss green, grey and sand brown. In spite of its official name, the sand brown was in fact a dark brown. The German vehicles that arrived in July-August 1944 remained in German dark yellow until 1945. This three-tone scheme had been used on Finnish artillery since 1941. Beginning in March 1942, Finnish tanks had tactical insignia painted on the turret, a square for the 1st Tank Company, a circle for the 2nd Tank Company and a triangle for the 3rd Tank Company. Individual vehicle numbers were painted inside these hollow signs, running from 0 to 15 (0 being the company commander, 1-5 being 1st platoon, and so

Right: Panther Ausf G, Zoska Battalion, Polish Home Army, Warsaw uprising, August 1944. This was one of two Panthers captured by the Polish insurgents and used during the fighting in Warsaw. It carries the name 'Pudel' and the national szachownica (chequer-board design) red and white insignia. The white fleur-de-lis is the insignia of the Polish Boy Scouts (Grey Ranks), which captured and manned the tank. The letters WP on the rear hatch stand for Wojsko Polskie (Polish Army).

Left: T-70, 2nd Tank Regiment, 1st Polish Armoured Brigade, August 1944. This T-70 has such a small turret that the national insignia has had to be carried on the mantlet front instead of the usual place with the number on the turret side.

Right: T-34 Model 1943, 1st Czechoslovak Tank Battalion, summer 1943. This T-34 was named after Janosik, a folk hero in Polish and Slovak legends, somewhat akin to a Tatra mountains version of Robin Hood.

Left: T-34-85 Model 1944, 1st Polish Armoured Brigade, winter 1944/45. This tank has been camouflaged in an irregular whitewash pattern. The tactical number indicates that it belonged to the brigade's chief of staff.

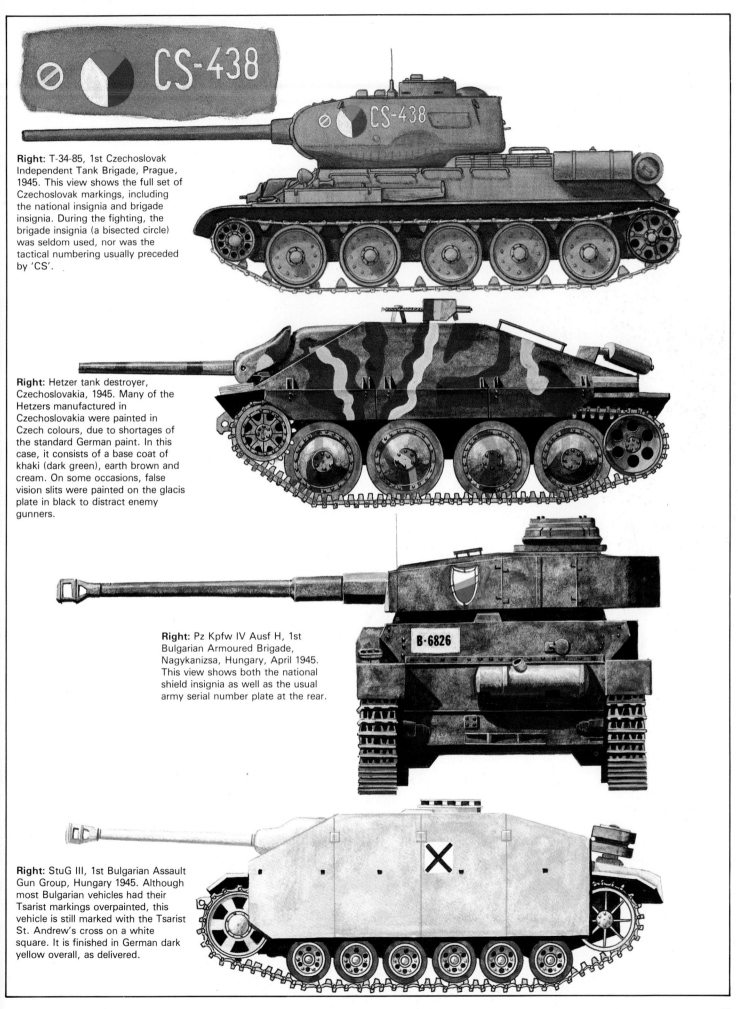

Right: T-34-85, 1st Czechoslovak Independent Tank Brigade, Prague, 1945. This view shows the full set of Czechoslovak markings, including the national insignia and brigade insignia. During the fighting, the brigade insignia (a bisected circle) was seldom used, nor was the tactical numbering usually preceded by 'CS'.

Right: Hetzer tank destroyer, Czechoslovakia, 1945. Many of the Hetzers manufactured in Czechoslovakia were painted in Czech colours, due to shortages of the standard German paint. In this case, it consists of a base coat of khaki (dark green), earth brown and cream. On some occasions, false vision slits were painted on the glacis plate in black to distract enemy gunners.

Right: Pz Kpfw IV Ausf H, 1st Bulgarian Armoured Brigade, Nagykanizsa, Hungary, April 1945. This view shows both the national shield insignia as well as the usual army serial number plate at the rear.

Right: StuG III, 1st Bulgarian Assault Gun Group, Hungary 1945. Although most Bulgarian vehicles had their Tsarist markings overpainted, this vehicle is still marked with the Tsarist St. Andrew's cross on a white square. It is finished in German dark yellow overall, as delivered.

Left: A BT-42 knocked out during the fighting in the summer of 1944. This vehicle is finished in the three tone camouflage scheme standard at this time, but the sand brown colour was nearly as dark as the moss green colour and is not clearly evident from photographs. This view clearly shows the later style of vehicle registration number on the hull rear. The BT-42 did not carry three-digit turret numbers. (George Balin)

Bottom left: The first StuG III received by Finland in the summer of 1943 at the Central Repair Works at Varkaus. This vehicle has had the new three-tone camouflage scheme applied, but has not yet had the typical Finnish modifications carried out, such as the addition of a stowage bin at the hull rear or the attachment of the spare road wheels on the hull sides. (Esa Muikku)

Top right: This StuG III (Ps 531-14), photographed in late summer 1944, has been heavily modified by adding log, concrete and appliqué armour to the extent that its markings are no longer very evident. While serving with the 2nd Company of the Assault Gun Battalion it scored six 'kills' against Soviet tanks, as is evident from the white bands on the gun barrel. It was later transferred to the 1st Tank Brigade as a training tank. (Esa Muikku)

Bottom right: A Pz Kpfw IV of the HQ, 2nd Tank Battalion in autumn 1944. Like most of the armoured vehicles obtained at the last moment in July 1944, there was not enough time to re-finish it in Finnish camouflage, and so it remained in German dark yellow with a light over-spray of dark green camouflage. Its registration number was Ps 221-15. (Esa Muikku)

on). Aside from this insignia, in the autumn of 1941 the 3rd Tank Company had adopted the skull and cross-bones as a unit insignia and the 2nd Company a dragon. These insignia were painted on the glacis plate, but began to disappear by the end of 1941. Finally, in 1943, a large three-digit tactical numbering system was adopted. The numbers were used in a method similar to the German system. The number 521 would indicate 5th Tank Company, 2nd platoon, 1st vehicle; 201 would indicate 2nd Tank Company, commanders's vehicle; 012 would indicate the second HQ tank of the 1st Tank Battalion.

Originally, Finnish tanks carried a one to three digit 'R-number' (Rekisteri numero-registration number). This was carried on a left side licence plate on the Vickers, but on other vehicles it could be seen painted fore and aft in either the left, right or centre position. These numbers ran from 0 through 906. In 1943, a different system was adopted. Each type of vehicle was given a two- or three-digit code preceded by the letters Ps (for panssarivaunu-armoured vehicle). This was followed by an individual vehicle number, such as Ps 245-8, the 245 being common to all T-34-85, and -8 indicating the eighth vehicle of this type in service. The registration number of each type is given in the table along with the number of vehicles of that type still in service in January 1945.

Registration numbers for armoured vehicle types in Finnish service as at 1 January 1945

Type	Serial	Total in service
BA-20	Ps 5, Ps 6	18
BA-10	Ps 25, Ps 26, Ps 27	23
T-26E	Ps 161	19
T-26 Model 1931	Ps 162	0
T-26 Model 1933	Ps 163	75 of Model 33 and Model 37
T-26 Model 1937	Ps 164	see preceding entry
T-50	Ps 183	1
T-34	Ps 231	7
T-28	Ps 241	7
T-34-85	Ps 245	7
KV-1 Model 1942	Ps 271	1
KV-1 (appliqué)	Ps 272	1
Landsverk Anti	Ps 455	6
BT-42	Ps 511	10
StuG III	Ps 531	47
T-38 training tank	Ps 601, 602	12
T-38 amphibious tank	—	3

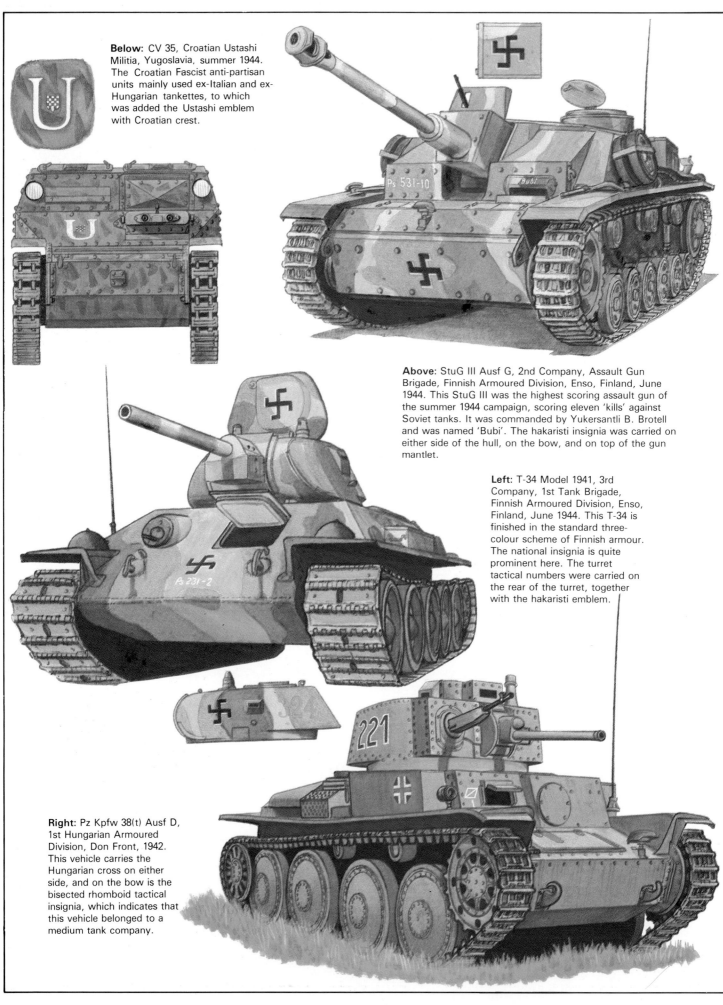

Below: CV 35, Croatian Ustashi Militia, Yugoslavia, summer 1944. The Croatian Fascist anti-partisan units mainly used ex-Italian and ex-Hungarian tankettes, to which was added the Ustashi emblem with Croatian crest.

Above: StuG III Ausf G, 2nd Company, Assault Gun Brigade, Finnish Armoured Division, Enso, Finland, June 1944. This StuG III was the highest scoring assault gun of the summer 1944 campaign, scoring eleven 'kills' against Soviet tanks. It was commanded by Yukersantli B. Brotell and was named 'Bubi'. The hakaristi insignia was carried on either side of the hull, on the bow, and on top of the gun mantlet.

Left: T-34 Model 1941, 3rd Company, 1st Tank Brigade, Finnish Armoured Division, Enso, Finland, June 1944. This T-34 is finished in the standard three-colour scheme of Finnish armour. The national insignia is quite prominent here. The turret tactical numbers were carried on the rear of the turret, together with the hakaristi emblem.

Right: Pz Kpfw 38(t) Ausf D, 1st Hungarian Armoured Division, Don Front, 1942. This vehicle carries the Hungarian cross on either side, and on the bow is the bisected rhomboid tactical insignia, which indicates that this vehicle belonged to a medium tank company.

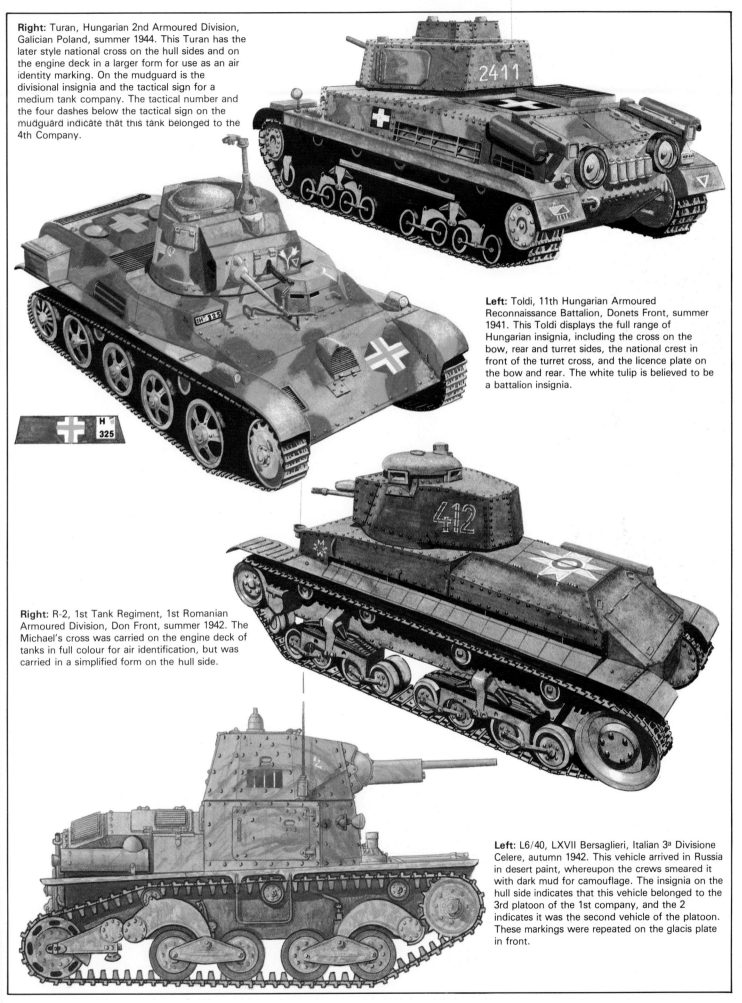

Right: Turan, Hungarian 2nd Armoured Division, Galician Poland, summer 1944. This Turan has the later style national cross on the hull sides and on the engine deck in a larger form for use as an air identity marking. On the mudguard is the divisional insignia and the tactical sign for a medium tank company. The tactical number and the four dashes below the tactical sign on the mudguard indicate that this tank belonged to the 4th Company.

Left: Toldi, 11th Hungarian Armoured Reconnaissance Battalion, Donets Front, summer 1941. This Toldi displays the full range of Hungarian insignia, including the cross on the bow, rear and turret sides, the national crest in front of the turret cross, and the licence plate on the bow and rear. The white tulip is believed to be a battalion insignia.

Right: R-2, 1st Tank Regiment, 1st Romanian Armoured Division, Don Front, summer 1942. The Michael's cross was carried on the engine deck of tanks in full colour for air identification, but was carried in a simplified form on the hull side.

Left: L6/40, LXVII Bersaglieri, Italian 3ª Divisione Celere, autumn 1942. This vehicle arrived in Russia in desert paint, whereupon the crews smeared it with dark mud for camouflage. The insignia on the hull side indicates that this vehicle belonged to the 3rd platoon of the 1st company, and the 2 indicates it was the second vehicle of the platoon. These markings were repeated on the glacis plate in front.

Hungary

Of all Germany's allies on the Eastern Front, the Hungarian Army deployed the largest armoured force and, apart from Italy, was the only ally with significant indigenous tank production. In 1938, Hungary acquired 104 CV 35 tankettes from Italy and began production under licence of the Swedish Landsverk L60B light tank, which was called the Toldi. The new Hungarian armoured units saw a small amount of fighting in the brief two-day war with Slovakia in March 1940, losing a few tankettes to air attack. Hungary entered the war on 10 April 1941 and participated with Germany in the invasion of Yugoslavia. At the time, the 1st and 2nd Motorized Brigade and the 2nd Cavalry Brigade each had an armoured reconnaissance battalion with a company of 20 Toldi light tanks, a company of 20 CV 35 tankettes and a company of 10 Alvis Straussler Csaba armoured cars. These units were the 9th, 11th and 3rd Armoured Reconnaissance Battalions respectively. Hungary entered the war with the Soviet Union on 27 June 1941, and the three brigades formed the Gyorshadtest (Fast Corps) with a total of 81 Toldis, 48 Csabas and 60 CV 35 tankettes. During the drive on the Donets River, the Hungarian units suffered severe equipment losses. Hungarian armoured vehicles of the period were not durable enough, nor were they heavily armed or armoured enough to stand up to the Soviet weapons. In October 1941, the Hungarian General Staff laid the groundwork for two armoured divisions and a mechanized cavalry division. Due to the delay in the production of the new Turan medium tank, the Hungarians were obliged to purchase armoured equipment from the Germans in order to field the 1st Armoured Division in 1942. A total of 8 Pz Kpfw I Ausf B, 102 Pz Kpfw 38(t) and 22 Pz Kpfw IV Ausf D were obtained, and these were used by the 1st Motorized Brigade to form the 1st Hungarian Armoured Division. The unit fought in the Don campaign in 1942, on the left flank of the German drive on Stalingrad. In January 1943 it was smashed by the Soviet counter-offensive, with only six tanks surviving to return to Hungary with the division in March 1943.

In the meantime, the 2nd Hungarian Armoured Division was being formed using the new Turan tanks and other Hungarian equipment, and plans were underway to equip the 1st Cavalry Division. In April 1944, the 2nd Armoured Division was sent into action in Galicia in eastern Poland. It was quite clear that the new Turans were inadequate to face T-34-85s, and the Germans finally consented to sell Hungary some more modern tanks, including a handful of Panthers and Tigers. However, when the 1st Cavalry Division went into action in June 1944 in eastern Poland, it was still equipped solely with the outdated Hungarian vehicles, not receiving its first Marder tank destroyers until August 1944.

The Germans occupied Hungary in March 1944, nearly putting an end to Hungarian vehicle production. The Germans forced the Hungarians to commit the remainder of its units to the Eastern Front, which included the new assault artillery battalions equipped with Turan tanks or Zrinyi or StuG III assault guns. Hungarian armoured units remained in action on the

Top left: Three companies of Hungarian CV 35 tankettes fought on the Eastern Front in 1941. Some of the surviving vehicles were later turned over to Croatian anti-partisan units. These CV 35s clearly show the three-tone camouflage in effect at the time, as well as the tricoloured national cross and the national crest immediately behind the side screen. (Batory Istvan)

Bottom left: A Pz Kpfw 38(t) Ausf D of the Hungarian 1st Armoured Division during fighting on the Don in 1942. On this particular vehicle, the national crosses have been over-painted and even the national crest on the licence plate obliterated, probably for security reasons. The three-digit tactical numbers on the turret followed the German practice of indicating company-platoon-vehicle. (Batory Istvan)

Top right: The Hungarian Army license-produced the Krupp Protze Kfz 70. This example from the 1st Armoured Division is seen here towing a 40mm 40M anti-tank gun, a weapon that was derived from the German PaK 36 but with a 40mm Bofors tube. The tactical insignia for an anti-tank company is clearly evident on the Protze. In the background is a Hungarian Pz Kpfw 38(t). (Batory Istvan)

Centre right: During the bitter fighting around Stalingrad, Hungarian vehicles were finished in whitewash, as is the case with this Pz Kpfw 38(t). The Hungarian 1st Armoured Division was virtually wiped out during the Soviet Stalingrad counter-offensive.

Bottom right: A pair of Csaba armoured cars negotiate a small bridge in eastern Poland in the summer of 1944. It is believed that the triangle insignia evident here was used by the 2nd Armoured Division. Next to it is an eagle emblem, probably of the reconnaissance company to which this vehicle belongs. The national insignia is on both the hull side and rear engine deck. (Batory Istvan)

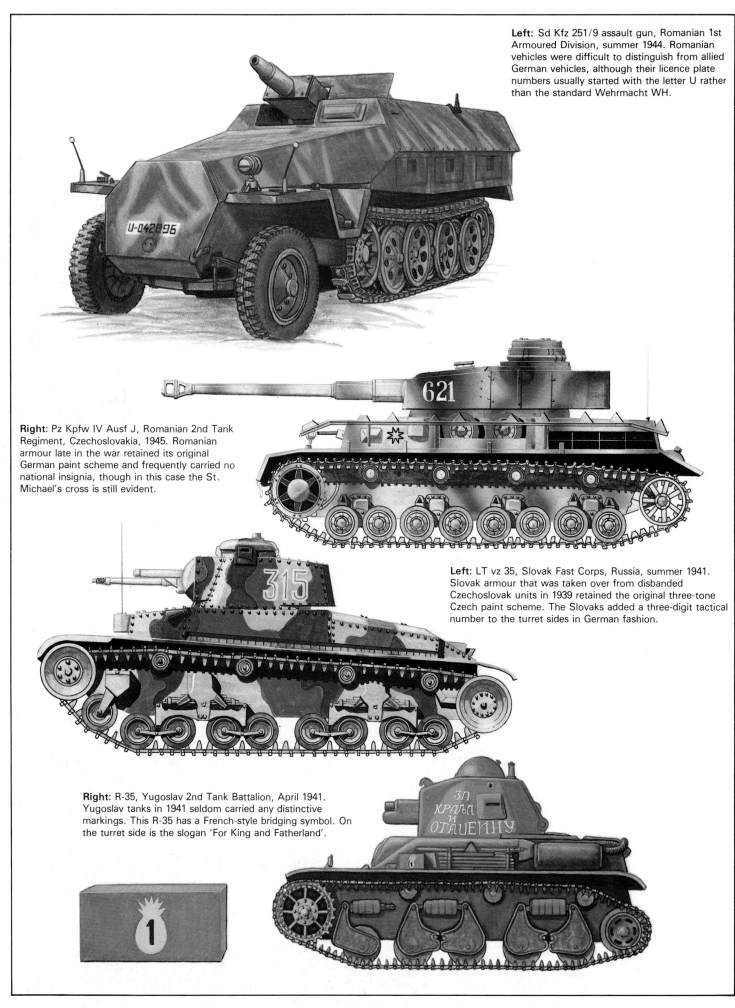

Left: Sd Kfz 251/9 assault gun, Romanian 1st Armoured Division, summer 1944. Romanian vehicles were difficult to distinguish from allied German vehicles, although their licence plate numbers usually started with the letter U rather than the standard Wehrmacht WH.

Right: Pz Kpfw IV Ausf J, Romanian 2nd Tank Regiment, Czechoslovakia, 1945. Romanian armour late in the war retained its original German paint scheme and frequently carried no national insignia, though in this case the St. Michael's cross is still evident.

Left: LT vz 35, Slovak Fast Corps, Russia, summer 1941. Slovak armour that was taken over from disbanded Czechoslovak units in 1939 retained the original three-tone Czech paint scheme. The Slovaks added a three-digit tactical number to the turret sides in German fashion.

Right: R-35, Yugoslav 2nd Tank Battalion, April 1941. Yugoslav tanks in 1941 seldom carried any distinctive markings. This R-35 has a French-style bridging symbol. On the turret side is the slogan 'For King and Fatherland'.

Above: A Toldi light tank, probably of the Hungarian 2nd Armoured Division, negotiates a partially demolished bridge in eastern Poland in the summer of 1944. The Toldi was a license-built version of the Swedish L60. Note the later-style Hungarian national cross on the hull side and on the rear engine deck. (Batory Istvan)

Right: A Turan tank crests a ridge during the brutal fighting in Galicia in the summer of 1944. Some Hungarian armoured vehicles during this period were left in dark green overall, and some Csabas in dark sand overall. The divisional insignia of the 2nd Armoured Division has been covered with mud, as has the national insignia on the hull side and the tactical number on the turret rear. Only the national cross insignia on the engine deck remains in evidence. (Batory Istvan)

Eastern Front even after Hungary had been overrun, some of the units being gradually re-equipped with more modern German equipment to replace their Turans and Zrinyis lost in action.

Camouflage Painting

Hungarian armour manufactured in 1941 and later was finished in a 'French' style of camouflage consisting of a base colour of dark olive green with light ochre and red-brown blotches. Up to 1942, this disruptive camouflage was brush applied with hard-edged patterns of irregular blotches. However, in 1942 the Hungarians began to use spray equipment on the newer Turans and other types, giving the camouflage patterns a more diaphanous appearance. Some of the vehicles delivered in 1944 seem to have been left in a uniform dark green overall, and at least some Csaba armoured cars were delivered in light ochre overall. German-supplied vehicles were left in the original colours. In the case of the vehicles of the 1st Armoured Division in 1942, this was panzer grey overall, while later vehicles were supplied in dark yellow. There are few clear photographs of the German vehicles supplied after June 1944, so it is impossible to note if they were camouflage painted or if they sported Hungarian insignia.

National Insignia

In 1940, the Hungarians used a Maltese cross as national insignia. This was rarely used on armoured vehicles, but consisted of a white cross with a thin green border and a hollow red circle in the centre. From 1941 through 1943, the Hungarian vehicle insignia was a Balkan cross similar in shape and proportion to the German insignia. However, the Hungarian cross was green with a white border and had triangular red areas filling in the spaces between the arms. This insignia was often accompanied by the Hungarian coat of arms in red, white and green. In 1944 and 1945, the Hungarian ground units adopted the same insignia that had been used by the air force, a white cross on a black square. The positioning of the national insignia varied: on the Toldi, the early cross was carried on the sides of the turret and the glacis plate; while on the Pz Kpfw 38(t) and the Pz Kpfw IV, it was carried on the hull sides. The later cross was usually carried on either side of the hull on most armoured vehicles, and was usually repeated quite large on the rear engine deck for air identification. Many of the vehicles of the 2nd Armoured Division in Galicia in 1944 had the national cross painted over or covered with mud, probably because it made a good aiming point for Soviet anti-tank gunners.

Left: Dawn in Galician Poland, summer 1944, as the crews of a Nimrod AA battery awake and man their vehicles. The Hungarian Army had hoped to use its Nimrods for anti-tank defence, but they were too poorly armed. These vehicles belong to the 1st Cavalry Division, and the divisional insignia is carried on the mudguards and the hull side in front of the cross. However, in this view it is obscured by the foliage being used for camouflage. Hungarian armour after 1942 usually used four-digit turret numbers carried only on the turret rear. (Batory Istvan)

Bottom left: This Hungarian Pz Kpfw III is finished in German dark yellow overall and only the Hungarian-style serial number identifies its nationality. (Ivan Bajtos)

Top right: A Pz Kpfw IV Ausf D of the Hungarian 1st Armoured Division during the Don campaign in 1942. The Hungarian tricoloured cross is carried on the rear and sides in much the same position as on German vehicles. The rear licence plate clearly identifies this as a Hungarian vehicle. In the upper left-hand corner above the licence plate is a bisected rhomboid insignia, indicative of a medium tank company. The vehicle's tactical number is carried on the rear and both sides of the turret stowage bin. (Batory Istvan)

Bottom right: This Hungarian Tiger I has no national insignia evident and is finished in German dark yellow overall. (Ivan Bajtos)

Unit Insignia

Hungarian armoured units appear to have used divisional insignia but, unfortunately, information on these insignia is scanty. The 1st Cavalry Division used a stylized white horseshoe design; the 2nd Armoured Division appears to have used a white triangle emblem; and the Ludovika Academy used a white angel in a shield. The 1st Armoured Division did not use any divisional insignia in 1942, but some of the sub-formations did use insignia, such as a map-derived tactical symbol for some of the anti-tank companies. Some of the Hungarian tactical insignia are shown in the accompanying illustrations and photographs.

Tactical Numbering

The units of the Fast Corps do not appear to have had turret tactical numbers in 1941. The 1st Armoured Division used large turret numbers in 1942 that were very similar to the three-digit German style. The 2nd Armoured Division used four-digit turret tactical numbering, painted in thin white numerals. This was usually only carried on the rear of the turret. Hungarian armour also had a regular system of vehicle licence plates very similar in appearance to the German style. The front serial was carried in a thin white rectangle. The pattern was usually 1H, the national shield, followed by a three-digit serial. The 1H referred to Honved (Army); the national shield was a simple badge in the green/white/red national colours; and the numbers were usually painted in black. The same details were carried on the rear licence plate, but this insignia was usually almost square in shape and was carried on the rear of the hull. In 1944, a subdued version of this insignia was used without the white background. The licence plate simply consisted of a thin black outline of the insignia with the serial number in black and the shield in the usual colours.

Other Markings

The Hungarians occasionally made use of tactical map symbols, using various rhomboid designs for armoured and mechanized formations. Some Hungarian armoured vehicles, notably the Zrinyi self-propelled guns, carried personal names painted on the glacis plate.

Italy

Although Italy employed many tank and cavalry units in the anti-partisan role in the Balkans, it made no major contribution of armour elsewhere on the Eastern Front. The only major units were those of the 3ª Divisione Celere with its LXVII Battaglione Bersaglieri Corazzato (with L6/40 light tanks) and the XIII Gruppo Semoventi (with a squadron of Semoventi da 47/32).

The L6/40 tanks and the 47/32 Semoventis were finished in dark yellow sand colour overall (giallo sabbia scuro), which proved to be less than ideal in the Russian terrain. As a result, mud was often smeared over the tanks to provide some camouflage. Markings were of the standard Italian variety. National insignia consisted of a large white circle carried on the turret roofs of the L6/40s for air identification. Licence plates were carried

fore and aft with the vehicle serial prefaced by RE (Royal Army). On the L6/40 and Semoventi da 47/32, the front licence consisted of two thin white rectangles with numbers in black, and on the rear a single rectangular plate. The standard unit block insignia was also employed. This consisted of a coloured rectangle, the colour indicating the company. The 1st company was red, the 2nd pale blue, the 3rd yellow, the 4th green and HQ white. These rectangles were divided by white bars, one for 1st platoon, two for 2nd, and so on. The HQ used black bars instead. This insignia was carried on the turret sides of the L6/40 and the superstructure sides of the 47/32, and on the hull front of both types. The individual vehicle number was carried in black on the front side of the L6/40 turret.

Below: A Soviet PTRD anti-tank gunner poses beside his victim, an Italian L6/40 light tank of the LXVII Battaglione Bersaglieri Corazzato. The four white stripes on the turret insignia indicate the fourth platoon, and the black '1' indicates first vehicle of the platoon. The colour of the rectangle indicates the company. This insignia was repeated on the hull front as well. Barely evident at the bottom of the photograph is the vehicle's serial number (RE 3882).

Poland

In 1943, the Soviet Union began forming a pro-Soviet Polish Army on Russian soil, distinct from the Polish Army fighting in Western Europe with Britain. The new Polish Army was called the LWP (Polish People's Army) and armoured units were raised, organized and equipped along Soviet lines. It would eventually field one tank corps (1 Korpus Pancery), two independent tank brigades (1 Brygada Pancerna, 16 Brygada Pancerna), two heavy tank regiments (4 Pulk Ciezki Czolgow, 5 Pulk Ciezki Czolgow) as well as numerous self-propelled gun and other armoured formations, entering combat at Lenino in 1943. During the Berlin operation, Polish troops made up nearly 10 per cent of Soviet forces in the assault.

National Insignia
The insignia adopted by tank units of the LWP was the Piast eagle, which was painted in white on tank turrets or on the superstructure sides of vehicles such as the SU-76 or ISU-152. There were a number of variations in the design, and some units altered the insignia to identify brigades. For example, in the 1st Armoured Corps, the 2nd and 4th Armoured Brigades added a white circle around the eagle, while the 3rd Armoured Brigade painted it on a red background with two white circles around it. The 16th Armoured Brigade placed it within a broken circle, while the 1st Armoured Brigade carried the eagle without any further decoration. The 4th Heavy Tank Regiment carried the eagle on a red diamond.

Tactical Numbering
The tanks and self-propelled guns of the LWP had a standardized numbering system in each unit, but the style varied from unit to unit. In the 1st Armoured Corps, each of the three battalions numbered their vehicles with four-digit figures. The first digit indicated the battalion (1–3), the second the company (1–2 in the 1st battalion, 3–4 in the 2nd battalion, 5–6 in the 3rd battalion), the third indicated the platoon (1–3) and the last indicated the vehicle (0 for company HQ, 1–3 in the 1st platoon, 4–6 in the 2nd platoon, 7–9 in the 3rd platoon). Therefore, 3212 indicated a tank of the 3rd battalion, 2nd company, 1st platoon, 2nd vehicle.

The 1st Armoured Brigade used three-digit numbers (except for the brigade HQ which used 1000 and 1001)

Top left: The tank crew commanded by Lieutenant Mateus Lach, commander of the 3rd Platoon, 1st Company, 2nd Tank Regiment, 1st Polish Tank Brigade, beside their T-34 Model 43 tank. The Piast eagle national insignia is very evident in this view together with the tactical number. Lach and his crew were credited with thirteen tank 'kills', and their tank is currently memorialized at the site of the Studianki battlefield in Poland where it fought in August 1944.

Bottom left: An ISU-152 of the Polish 13th SP Artillery Regiment during a parade in Warsaw in celebration of the victory over Germany. Polish self-propelled artillery frequently had the tactical numbers carried on the superstructure front as well as the usual positions on the side.

Top right: A T-34-85 of the Polish 1st Armoured Brigade in the port of Gdynia in March 1945 after the heavy fighting there. This vehicle still has traces of its winter whitewash. The Piast eagle is carried on the turret front.

Bottom right: An IS-2m heavy tank of the Polish 4th Heavy Tank Regiment during the fighting in East Prussia in March 1945. The 4th Heavy Tank Regiment used a white eagle within an oblong red diamond as its unit insignia.

with the first number (in 1944) indicating the regiment (1–2), or in 1945 indicating the battalion (1–3), the second number indicated the company, and the third number indicated the platoon and individual vehicle in the same fashion as mentioned above for the 1st Armoured Corps. The 16th Armoured Brigade used four-digit numbers, the first indicating the battalion, the second the company, the third the platoon, and the fourth the vehicle (1–3). The 4th Heavy Tank Regiment used four-digit numbers beginning with '4' until March 1945 when it reverted to a three-digit number also beginning with '4'. The first number was the same throughout the regiment, the second indicated the company and the third indicated the vehicle and platoon (1–2 first platoon, 3–4 second platoon). The 5th Heavy Tank Regiment used four-digit numbers beginning with '5'. The second number indicated the company, the third indicated the platoon, and the fourth indicated the vehicle. The self-propelled gun regiments generally used three-digit numbers. A number was assigned to each of the regiments which was used as the first digit; for example, 3 was used by the 13th SP Artillery Regiment (SU-85), 8 was used by the 28th SP Artillery Regiment, 2 by the 2nd SP Artillery Detachment. In the regiments, the second digit usually indicated the battery, while in the small SU-76 detachments the vehicles were simply numbered consecutively.

Other Markings

During the Warsaw uprising of 1944, Polish Home Army forces, besides LWP armoured units, captured several German tanks which were used in the fighting. These vehicles remained in German colours, but had various names, militia insignia and national insignia added. Some of these are shown in the photographs and illustrations.

Top left: A German Sd Kfz 250/10 captured by the Polish 13th SP Artillery Regiment. The vehicle was impressed into Polish service and, after their insignia were added, it was used for reconnaissance during the fighting in Pomerania in 1945.

Bottom left: A T-34 Model 43, probably of the 4th Heavy Tank Regiment, during the Berlin operation in April 1945. The Soviet-style white turret band and roof cross have been added hastily, almost completely over-painting the national eagle insignia.

Top centre: An SU-85 of the Polish 13th SP Artillery Regiment in action in May 1945. This shows a rare combination of the April turret stripe and roof cross, which the crew has attempted to strip off prior to adding the May white triangle identity marking. The white triangle can be seen on the hull side and would have been repeated on the roof, over the scraped remnants of the earlier cross insignia. Also evident on the hull side is the national white eagle at the rear, and the vehicle number (311), which was repeated on the left hull front over the driver's hatch. This particular vehicle was knocked out during the fighting against the Pomeranian wall in February 1945, but was rebuilt and returned to action.

Top right: 'Chwat' was one of the armoured vehicles captured by the Polish Home Army during the August 1944 uprising. Besides this Hetzer, the Poles also captured several Panthers, an Sd Kfz 251 and a number of other armoured vehicles, even an ex-Italian M13/40.

Right: An SU-76M of the Polish 27th SP Artillery Regiment, 1st Armoured Corps during the victory parade in Warsaw after the war. Several of the sub-units of the 1st Armoured Corps used a circled eagle to distinguish themselves from other Polish armoured units.

Romania

In 1941, the Romanian armoured force consisted of about 35 Czech R-1 tankettes, 126 Czech R-2 light tanks (LT vz 35, or Pz Pkfw 35(t)), 73 Renault R-35s and 60 obsolete FT-17s. The R-2s formed the 1st Tank Regiment, the R-35s formed the 2nd Tank Regiment, and the R-1s were used by the 1st Royal Cavalry Division. The R-35s had been obtained in part when the Polish 21st Armoured Battalion had been interned in 1939. However, there were inadequate spare parts to support this unit, and when the 1st Royal Armoured Division was formed and sent into action in the Soviet Union in 1941, it went without the R-35s. After fighting during the drive on Odessa and the 1942 Don campaign, the unit's tanks were badly worn, and in September 1942 it was reinforced with 11 Pz Kpfw III Ausf N and 11 Pz Kpfw IVs purchased from Germany. The 1st Royal Armoured Division was virtually wiped out in the Stalingrad débâcle where the old R-2s faced T-34s on very unequal terms. The Germans hastily provided 50 Pz Kpfw 38(t)s in March 1943 to keep the 1st Tank Regiment in the field and, from November 1943, began providing 129 Pz Kpfw IVs and 114 StuG IIIs to reconstitute the division. Besides these German vehicles, in 1942 the Brasov factory began modifying a number of surviving R-2 tanks by the addition of captured Soviet ZiS-3 76mm field-guns. Later, the Germans provided the Romanians with several dozen captured T-60 light tanks which had Soviet F-22 76.2mm divisional guns added in an open casemate mount. These vehicles were used as tank destroyers and were designated TACAM (Tun autopropulsat cu afet mobile 76.2mm) R-2 or T-60. Some of the R-2 versions were later armed with the 75mm system Resite Model 1943, which was essentially a ZiS-3 rechambered to accept German 75mm ammunition. The 1st Armoured Division remained in action alongside the Wehrmacht until August 1944,

Top: These Romanian R-1 tanks at the CKD factory in Czechoslovakia in 1940 show the crest of King Carol II on their turrets. With King Michael I's accession to the throne in 1941, the Romanian vehicle insignia switched to the Michael's cross. (Ivan Bajtos)

Above: An R-2 of the Romanian 1st Armoured Division in Russia, 1941. The Michael's cross is carried on the hull side in white. The full colour cross can be partly seen on the open engine deck cover.

Left: The R-2 remained the backbone of the Romanian tank force until the winter of 1942/43 when the division was virtually destroyed outside Stalingrad. This R-2 has had a hasty whitewash finish applied to the turret sides. (National Archives)

when Antonescu was overthrown and Romania switched sides. The 2nd Tank Regiment with about 66 Pz Kpfw IV and R-35 tanks and 80 other armoured vehicles (mostly Hanomag Sd Kfz 251 and self-propelled guns) fought in Czechoslovakia, ending the war near Vienna. Towards the end of the war, the Soviets supplied small numbers of T-34-85 tanks, but Romanian equipment remained primarily of German origin.

Until 1940, Romanian tanks had the crest of King Carol II painted on the turret, thereafter, during the war years, the cross of King Michael I was used instead. This was first applied during the 1941 campaign. Usually, a small white stencilled cross was carried on the hull side in white and a white/yellow/red cross carried on the engine deck for air identification. Romanian tanks were usually in the colour of the original manufacturer, which in the case of the R-35s was dark French Army green, and in the case of the R-1s and R-2s was Czech olive drab. The German Pz Kpfw 38(t)s received in 1943 were in panzer grey, while the remainder of the German armoured equipment received later was in dark yellow with sprayed olive green or red-brown on occasion. The 1st Armoured Division used large white trim turret tactical numbers in 1942. In 1944 they seem to have used thin black or white three-digit numbers, in the cases where numbers were used at all. Indeed, after 1943 markings do not seem to have been commonplace on Romanian armoured vehicles. Some photographs show the Michael's cross in black on the lighter dark yellow background, but many vehicles appear to have gone unmarked. Many Romanian Army vehicles carried a German-style serial number on the front plate, consisting of a thin white rectangle with a serial number in black preceded by the letter U. In some cases, the colours on this licence plate were reversed. Romanian armoured vehicles do not appear to have used divisional insignia. The vehicles of the 2nd Tank Regiment that fought alongside the Soviets in Czechoslovakia in 1944–45 used a white circle with red star as their national insignia.

Right: An example of a tun autopropulsat cu afet mobil 76.2mm, a Romanian conversion based on a captured Soviet T-60 light tank and an F-22 gun. The type was finished in dark green, but seldom carried any markings. On some occasions the Romanian cross was carried on the rear deck ammunition bin, which this vehicle is without.

Bottom left: The 2nd Romanian Tank Regiment, which fought alongside the Soviets in Czechoslovakia in 1945 was equipped with Pz Kpfw IV and R-35 tanks. Many of the old R-35 tanks were re-armed with captured Soviet 45mm anti-tank guns, as is the case with this vehicle in Brno in 1945. The 2nd Tank Regiment used a white circle with red star as a national marking during this fighting. (Ivan Bajtos)

Bottom right: Romanian Pz Kpfw IVs of the 2nd Tank Regiment near Nagykaroly, Hungary, in 1944 after Romania had joined the war against the Germans. These vehicles were finished in typical German fashion, and often carried no national insignia.

Slovakia

After their absorption of Czechoslovakia in 1938, the Germans permitted the formation of a Fascist puppet state in the eastern Slovak provinces in March 1939. Slovakia was permitted an army which would be equipped from the matériel of the former Czechoslovak Army remaining on Slovak soil. The former Czechoslovak 3rd Fast Division had left 79 Skoda LT vz 35 tanks in the Levice area and this formed the basis of the new Slovak Fast Division. After the Slovak participation in the 1939 invasion of Poland, the unit was given a further 30 CKD vz 33 tankettes and 13 OA vz 30 armoured cars. The Slovaks intended to build up the unit along the lines of the original Czechoslovak Fast Divisions, but the Germans initially were quite reluctant to supply enough vehicles. Finally, a further 32 Pz Kpfw 38(t) Ausf S and 21 LT vz 40 light tanks were supplied.

The border dispute between Slovakia and Hungary erupted into a short war in March 1939 during the course of which the Slovaks lost at least one LT vz 35. The Slovak Fast Corps took part in the 1941 invasion of the Soviet Union, fighting at Lvov and Kiev. During the Caucasus fighting after Stalingrad, the Fast Division was nearly wiped out and was evacuated minus all its armoured equipment. The Germans began efforts to rebuild the Army with the supply of 37 Pz Kpfw 38(t)s, 7 Pz Kpfw III Ausf N, 16 Pz Kpfw II Ausf F and 18 Sd Kfz 138 Marder tank destroyers. However, in late August 1944, a military coup was staged launching the Slovak uprising against the Germans. The insurgents had a significant portion of remaining Slovak armour, including about 30 light tanks, 12 Marders and at least 1 Pz Kpfw III. Also, they built three armoured trains using LT vz 35 tank turrets for armament. The rising

Above: A Slovak OA vz 30 armoured car operating in the Ukraine in 1941. Evident on the turret is the double-armed Slovak cross carried on some vehicles in 1941. (Ivan Bajtos)

Left: A Slovak Pz Kpfw III Ausf N in the Caucasus in 1943. This vehicle is finished in dark yellow overall and would have the tricolour Slovak crest on the side of the turret armour. Slovak tanks fighting in the 1944 uprising were marked similarly. (Ivan Bajtos)

Above: An LT vz 38 of the Slovak Fast Corps on parade in 1940. It is finished in the Czech three-colour scheme. The licence plate is clearly evident in this view. (Ivan Bajtos)

Above right: A Slovak LT vz 40 command tank in Russia, 1941. Note that a German flag was used for air identification.

Right: Tanks of the Slovak Fast Corps in the Ukraine in 1941. In the background are a number of LT vz 35 in Czech three-colour camouflage with red three-digit turret numbers heavily bordered in white. In the foreground is an LT vz 40, which is painted in panzer grey overall since it was manufactured after the German annexation of Czechoslovakia.

was finally crushed before the insurgents could link up with Soviet troops.

The Slovak Army's original armoured equipment was finished in its original Czechoslovak colours of olive drab, sand and red-brown. They were marked with Czechoslovak serials, which were thin black rectangles with white numerals in the 13–540 to 13–963 range. The later shipments of equipment manufactured under German control, such as the Pz Kpfw 38(t)s and the LT vz 40s, were supplied in panzer grey. They carried the new-style serials, which numbered V-3001 through V-3131 (V for Voiska, or Army) and, as in the case of the Czechoslovak serials, these rectangles were carried on the bow and centrally on the rear plate. The new vehicles had the double-armed Slovak cross painted in white on the front of the turret side, while the older tanks had white and red three-digit numerals painted on the rear of the turret sides. In 1942, these markings gave way to the national shield, which was blue, white and red. The last batch of equipment received from the Germans had the black serial rectangles and the national shield, but were left in their original German dark yellow finish. The three armoured trains built during the Slovak uprising were finished in the tricolour pre-war camouflage.

Yugoslavia

The Yugoslav Army had two tank battalions with a third in formation prior to the German invasion in the spring of 1941. The I Bataljon bornih kola (I Bbk) consisted of 48 French FT-17s and NC-27s with a squadron of 8 Czechoslovak S-Id tankettes. The II Bbk was to be formed with 50 French Renault R-35s purchased in February 1940, but it is not known how many actually arrived prior to the fall of France. The III Bbk was supposed to be formed with Polish 7TP light tanks, but these plans had to be dropped with the collapse of Poland in 1939. Instead, the unit was formed in the Soviet Union with BT-7 tanks, but was not ready to be returned to Yugoslavia in time for the 1941 fighting. The few surviving photographs of Yugoslav armour during this period would seem to indicate that the vehicles were left in the colour of the manufacturers; in the case of the French equipment in dark French Army green overall, and in the case of the Czechoslovak tankettes in a tricolour camouflage of olive drab, sand and red-brown. Except for a few tanks with slogans chalked on them, no national insignia or other markings seem to have been carried.

Although the Yugoslav Army ceased to exist, many partisan units sprang up in the Serbian and Croatian provinces. The Communist partisans under Tito eventually built up the largest tank force employed by any resistance organization in Europe during the Second World War. They captured their first tank, a French Hotchkiss H-39, in September 1941. Several dozen more were captured during the war, mainly French light tanks such as the H-39 and R-35, Italian CV 33 and CV 35 tankettes and French Somuas being used by German and Italian anti-partisan units. In fact, by 1944 the partisans had several tank 'battalions' equipped with over a dozen tanks each. In July 1944, the partisans formed the 1st Tank Brigade with the aid of the British

Top left: A Slovak LT vz 38 in 1942 in panzer grey overall with the national crest on the turret side in white/light blue/red. (Ivan Bajtos)

Left: Yugoslav S-Id tankettes of the 1 Bbk on manoeuvres before the outbreak of the war. These vehicles were finished in the same colours as other Czech-manufactured vehicles: khaki (dark green) with cream and brown patches.

Bottom left: The partisan units of the Titoist forces captured several dozen tanks during the savage guerrilla war in Yugoslavia, in this case an Italian L6/40. Some had a white circle with red star or a plain white star added as national insignia, while others carried the name of their militia painted on the side. This vehicle still remains in the Italian scheme of brick red with dark green blotches.

Top right: The 1st Yugoslav Tank Brigade was raised with British aid and landed on the Dalmatian coast in 1944. This M3A3 light tank is being serviced by its crew. It was finished in US olive drab with field drab bands. On the hull side is the national flag in blue/white/red with a red star in the centre, and red stars can be seen on the glacis and mudguard.

Right: An NC-1 (foreground) and FT-17 of the 1st Yugoslav Tank Battalion knocked out during the fighting in 1941. These tanks generally were unmarked except for French-style bridging symbols. (National Archives)

Army at Bari on the Italian Adriatic coast. It consisted of 56 M3A1 and M3A3 Stuart light tanks originally, and 24 AEC Mark III and IV armoured cars in four battalions, though its strength was raised later to 75 Stuarts. With Anglo-American naval support, the brigade was landed on the Dalmatian coast in November 1944, whereupon it began to fight its way north to Trieste. During the drive through Yugoslavia, several Stuarts were turned into improvised self-propelled guns by removing their turrets and adding captured German PaK40 75mm anti-tank guns or quad 20mm FlaK38 anti-aircraft guns. Vehicles of this unit were finished in olive drab with bands of field-brown disruptive camouflage

paint. National insignia in the form of the tricoloured national flag (blue/white/red with a red star centred in the white field) was carried on the turret or hull sides.

In the meantime, the 2nd Tank Brigade was formed in the Soviet Union, equipped along Soviet lines with 65 T-34-85 tanks. This unit took part in the liberation of Zagreb and met up with the 1st Tank Brigade in Trieste. Its vehicles were finished in dark Soviet Army green overall. Most vehicles carried a three-digit white turret number, and some had a red star painted on the turret front. These red stars, in Yugoslav style, had thicker arms than usual. Some vehicles also had slogans chalked on the turret.

Left: The 2nd Yugoslav Tank Brigade was raised in the USSR with T-34-85 tanks. Here, a vehicle of the unit drives into Trieste in 1945. It has the slogan 'Na Berlin' ('To Berlin') painted on the side of the turret.

Select Bibliography

It is not the intention of the authors to list all of the published works consulted in the course of research on this book, since in the case of the Soviet Union alone this would run to over one hundred books. Rather, mention is made here of the major books or articles dealing with tank markings, although we have included several general articles on the armoured forces of some of the small countries for readers who may wish to pursue the matter further.

Germany
Culver, B. *Panzer Colours*, Arms & Armour Press, London, 1977; Squadron/Signal Publications, Carrollton, 1977.
– *Panzer Colours II*, Arms & Armour Press, London, 1978; Squadron/Signal Publications, Carrollton, 1978
Hartmann, T. *Wehrmacht Divisional Signs 1938–1945*, Almark, London, 1970
Martinetti, J. *Les signes tactiques de l'Axe*, DeBello, Paris, 1976
Murphy, W. 'Deployment of Ferdinand/Elefant Units', *AFV News*, Vol. 15, No. 2.
– 'Tiger Formations: An inspection of deployment and markings', *AFV News*, Vol. 14, No. 3
Sohns, A. 'German Tactical (Map) Symbols in WWII', *AFV News*, Vol. 8, No. 1
Steuard, J. 'StuG Brigade Histories', *AFV-G2*, Vol. 1, No. 9–Vol. 12, No. 6
– 'Tactical Markings of the Waffen SS', *AFV-G2*, Vol. 1, No. 4–No. 9
Tomioka, Y. et al. *German Vehicle Markings*, Sunday Art Publications, Tokyo, 1980
Wiener, F. *Painting of Army Equipment 1939–45* (translated by D. Filby), unpublished manuscript, 1957

Soviet Union
Zaloga, S. 'Organization of the Soviet Armored Force 1939–45', *AFV News*, Vol. 16, No. 2
– 'Soviet Pre-War AFV Markings', *Military Modelling*, December 1982.
– 'Soviet Tank Markings, 1930–45', *AFV News*, Vol. 9, Nos. 6 and 7.

Bulgaria
Kalamov, C. 'Avtobronevo technicesko osigujavane na BNA prez Otecestvenata vojna 1940–44', *Voenny istoristechny Sbornik*, R.49/2

Czechoslovakia
Ceskoslovenske Tankove Vojsko c SSSR, Nase Vojsko, Prague, 1978
Holub, O. *Ceskoslovenske tanky a tankiste*, Nase Vojsko, Prague, 1980

Finland
Kantakoski, P. *Suomalaiset panssarivauno joukot 1919–1969*, Hameenlinna, 1969
Muikku, E. 'The 6-ton Vickers in Finland', *IPMS Mallari*, November 1976.
Zaloga, S. and K. Rosenlof. 'Finnish Armour', *Airfix Magazine*, May 1976

Hungary
Dombrady, L. 'A Magyar pancelos magasabbegysegek kiepitesere tett erofeszitesek a habory idoszakban 1941–44', *Hadtortenelmi Kozlemenyek*, No. 2, 1961
Probst, J. 'Hungarian Armour in World War 2', *Airfix Magazine*, September 1976
– 'Hungarian Armor in World War 2', *AFV-G2*, Vol. 6, No. 4

Italy
Benvenuti, B. *Carri Armati 2/II*, Edizioni Bizzari, Rome, 1973

Slovakia
Doyle, H. and C. Kliment. 'The Slovak State 1939–45', *Military Journal*, Vol. 2.

Yugoslavia
Babic, M. *Oklopne jedinice U Nor-u*, Belgrade, 1968
Zaloga, S. 'Yugoslav Armored Units 1941–45', *AFV News*, Vol. 9, No. 1.